Musée national du Moyen Age

Thermes de Cluny

Musée national du

Moyen Age

Thermes de Cluny

Alain Erlande-Brandenburg
Museum Director

Pierre-Yves Le Pogam, Dany Sandron
Curators

Réunion
des Musées
Nationaux

Foreword

This guide illustrates and annotates about 230 works selected from the thousands of exhibits in the collection. Reorganisation of exhibition space or restoration work may prevent all the objects illustrated from being displayed at the same time. The works presented in the guide are designated on the Museum circuit by a blue spot

Exhibits are listed chronologically in each chapter, except for "Textiles", in which they appear according to technique and geographical provenance.

The dimensions of works are always given in centimetres.

Cover illustration:
Bust-reliquary of St.Mabilla
(n° 174)

ISBN 2-7118-2777-1
© Réunion des musées nationaux, Paris, 1993
49, rue Etienne-Marcel, 75001 Paris

Acknowledgements

The authors of this guide would like to thank
Roselyne Bussière,
Heritage Curator,
and Geneviève François,
researcher at C.N.R.S.

Contents

The courtyard

The Buildings

The Baths

The Gallo-Roman baths (*thermae*) are one of the most impressive vestiges of ancient architecture preserved on Gallic soil. Lutetia, as Paris was then called, was divided into two agglomerations: the Cité, surrounded by a protective wall in the IVth century, and the open town built by the Romans on the hillside currently known as Mount Sainte-Geneviève that slopes down to the Seine. The majestic river, without its embankments of today, stretched over a wide area. In the south, marshland extended as far as the present-day boulevard Saint-Germain, which determined the constructible limit. Villas and sumptuous monuments thus spread over the hillsides: the forum under the rue Soufflot; the southern baths; the eastern baths on the site of the Collège de France; finally, the northern baths, known as the Cluny baths.

The monument here was built on a platform of beaten earth to the south and over cellars on the north side, to compensate for the slope of the terrain, which was steeper than it is today. Although incomparable with the scale of the *Thermae* at Trier (170 m × 100 m), at that time capital of the

The Frigidarium

Empire, the architect had designed a vast, rectangular edifice (100 m × 65 m), flanked by shops, annexes and dwellings, to ensure the life and function of the building. Despite excavations carried out in the XIXth century under Théodore Vacquer, then after the Second World War by Messrs Duval and Trouvelot, and recent

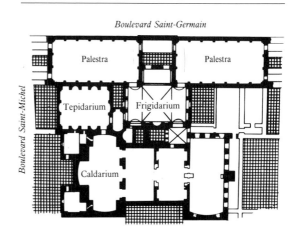

Floor-plan of the Roman baths

Mosaic probably from the Roman baths
Cl. 12523

swimming bath in the north, the orifice used to drain the water, the conduits running through the south wall and the groined rubblestone vault supported by solid corbels.

The visitor should picture this IIIrd-century architectural ensemble brought to life by water, in pools of different temperatures, and buzzing with the sound of Roman and Gallic voices intermingled with those of their slaves. It was, like many other *Thermae*, one of the high spots of Roman civilisation.

The house of the abbots of Cluny

The southern part of the town had been abandoned in the wake of the Barbarian invasions. It was here that the University established itself, at the beginning of the XIIIth century, in what would become known as the "Latin Quarter". The abbots of Cluny, like many others, endeavoured to acquire a school and a residence there. The former, built during the second half of the XIIIth century, stood on the present-day site of the place de la Sorbonne; the latter was near the baths. At the end of the XVth century, the abbot Jacques d'Amboise (1485-1510) decided to replace the house by a more fashionable residence. Construction was completed rapidly, even though the west wing was modified and pushed further west, and today the building represents the earliest example of a mansion between courtyard and garden. It was shut off from the town by a blind wall, broken only by a carriage gateway and a pedestrian entrance, and was built on a U-shaped plan, with the main building to the north, flanked by two side wings enclosing a courtyard. It is a two-storeyed building, topped by a high slate roof with dormer-windows, the lower part of which is hidden by an overhanging parapet. Three spiral staircases lead up to the upper floors, including the northern staircase on the main building in the centre. The gallery running along the west wing is open on the ground floor, but closed on the upper level. An additional wing, intended to house the cha-

surveys, questions are still raised concerning the disposition and interior design of the monument. It is more inconsistent than a first impression may suggest. The early first-century building later underwent thorough modifications: access was diverted from north to south and the intended use of certain rooms was altered. Three important rooms have however been identified without difficulty: the hot room - the *caldarium* - in the south, on the corner of the boulevard Saint-Michel and the rue du Sommerard; the warm room - the *tepidarium* - to the west, on the boulevard Saint-Michel; the cold room - the *frigidarium* - in the heart of the museum. The two former rooms are partially ruined, but are easily recognisable on their lower level, as are the two east and west palaestras (gymnasiums) facing the boulevard Saint-Germain. Certain heated and unheated rooms also found in the museum, in the basement or on a higher level, were probably used for meetings and as storerooms.

The upper-level walls still have their original facing that is conspicuous by the use of small square stones interspersed at regular intervals with rows of bricks. They were initially covered by mosaic, marble or paint. Traces can still be seen in the frigidarium, which has retained its fixtures: the

The Chapel. Print taken from «The Arts of the Middle Ages»

pel and its adjoining room, lies to the north and stretches west to enclose the private garden.

The original interior disposition of the mansion has been preserved: the spacious rooms, the passageway along the courtyard and above all the chapel that boasts an apse in the east and has retained its painted decor, attributed to Guido Mazzoni, and its sculptures in the cul-de-four, complementing the Entombment scene from which three heads have been found. The delicate support sustaining the ribs is an example of Late Gothic architecture. The recesses were initially intended to house statues of the Amboise family, renowned among other things for their activity in the artistic field.

The collections

The Museum's collections have been inventoried today at over 23,000 exhibits, but a large number were transferred to Ecouen on the creation of the Musée National de la Renaissance. The founding of the Musée des Thermes et de l'Hôtel de Cluny owed much to the Romantic movement, and to one man who embodied it: Alexandre Du Sommerard. The town greeted his project with enthusiasm and its subsequent curators showed untiring activity.

Born in 1779, at Bar-sur-Aube, Alexandre Du Sommerard opted for the military life at an early age, then joined the staff of the Cour des Comptes (State Audit Office) as chief clerk in 1807, moving up to the position of principal advisor by the end

The vault of the Chapel

of his career. At a time when an inordinate taste for Antiquity was dominant and the Medieval and Renaissance eras were little appreciated, not to say disdained, he developed a keen interest in these later periods. He immediately appeared as a forerunner in this speciality, while his curiosity extended to many other fields. To illustrate a large work in five volumes on *The Arts of the Middle Ages* (1838-1846), he used lithography, a process that was still in its infancy, but which enabled him to reproduce a great number of objects in his own and other collections. Following the example of theso-called "antiquarians," Deruge-Duménil, Revoil, Sauvageot and many others, he began to acquire objects, some of which have since proved to be great masterpieces. In order to make these purchases, in 1826 he had to sell a fine collection of drawings by old and modern masters. His collection rapidly became famous in Paris, for he moved in society and literary circles and was liberal in his invitations to visitors. *The Antiquarian,* an 1825 painting by Xavier Leprince, portrays Du Sommerard at his home, then in the rue Ménars, surrounded by his treasures. Their growing number soon obliged him to change house and when he moved to the mansion of the Cluny abbots, his choice proved to be an excellent one. Like Alexandre Lenoir, founder of the Musée des Monuments Français in the convent of the Petits-Augustins, he was imaginative enough to take advantage of the setting and to present his collection in a decor designed to impress his visitors. Contemporary engravings and paintings give us an idea of the care he took in its display. With an astonishing sense of theatre, he succeeded in evoking the memory of great figures from the past. François I, whom Sauvageot referred to as "his king", was particularly favoured: a whole room was devoted to him, containing his bed, his stirrups, and a host of other objects generously attributed to him. Elsewhere, techniques and periods intermingled, with the most varied objects juxtaposed in complete defiance of chronology, most of them associated with some illustrious origin. Some were less authentic

than Du Sommerard believed; several - like certain pieces of furniture - proved to be amazing fabrications, in which genuine wood panels were mixed with others created for the occasion. Fakes invariably slipped into this vast array of bric-à-brac, for methods of authentication at the time were a far cry from what they are today, and gullible buyers were an easy prey for clever forgers. Du Sommerard's contemporaries, aware of the relationship that had been established between this collection and the building in which it was housed, voiced their desire to see this association become permanent through the creation of a museum. At the 1833 Salon, Albert Lenoir, son of the founder of the Musée des Monuments Français, presented a "Project for a historical museum formed by uniting the Palais des Thermes and the Hôtel de Cluny". This idea met with enthusiastic acclaim, backed up by the existence of a stonework deposit the City of Paris had established in the frigidarium of the baths.

The Gallo-Roman baths, which had been proclaimed national property during the Revolution, had found no buyer, and so they were assigned to the hospice of Charenton in 1809. Even before then, concern for their preservation and use had been expressed by the so-called "*antiquomanes*", or enthusiasts of Antiquity. In 1807, Baltard had suggested that the frigidarium be emptied "in order to house sculptures executed in Paris or at least brought there by the Romans". Grivaud took up the idea of the creation of a museum again in 1809, followed, in 1817, by Quatremère de Quincy. In 1816, the closing of the Musée des Monuments Français founded under the Revolution by Alexandre Lenoir reinforced this trend in public opinion, added to which was the need to protect the sculptures that had been exhibited there. Alexandre Lenoir, hoping to see his former museum resurrected, was himself an earnest advocate of this idea. In 1819, Louis XVIII responded to this movement, ordering the ruins to be purchased and the *Thermae* to be cleared. He appointed a curator who had ancient sculptures transferred there. The State rapidly lost interest in the project that the City of Paris took over in 1836. Modelling itself on other great cities of the realm, Paris felt the need to have its own "museum of Gallic and Roman antiquities". Without delay, numerous sculptures from the demolition and restoration of Parisian buildings, or even from excavations, were deposited there. The success of this initiative owed much to the hope that the Du Sommerard collections next door would soon become national property.

The death of the famous collector, on 19 August 1842, was to accelerate this process. Through astute negotiations, the City assigned the *Thermae* and the stonework collections to the State on the condition that Edmond Du Sommerard, son of Alexandre, be appointed curator. On 1st July 1843, the Chambre des Députés voted for the purchase of the house and the collections. The law of 24 July 1843 officially ratified the creation of the "Musée des Thermes et de l'Hôtel de Cluny"; its curator was Edmond Du Sommerard, and its architect Albert Lenoir. During the lengthy debates that preceded this decision, the former Musée des Monuments Français was frequently evoked. Its memory hovered over the proceedings like a phantom presence to which it was hoped new substance could be given; there was also remorse, for its closing had caused considerable emotion. The opening of the new museum was a triumph. On 17 March 1844, the number of visitors reached 12,000, and on the following Sunday, 16,000. The merger of these two collections of widely different origins was to give the museum a character that it still retains today, one of extraordinary variety. The City donated the capitals from Saint-Germain-des-Près, the statues from Notre-Dame discovered in 1839 in the rue de la Santé, as well as the ancient fragments that were previously in the Musée des Monuments Français: the blocks of the Pillar of the Nautes, the bull of Saint-Marcel. The second group of works consisted of the 1,494 objects in the Du Sommerard collection, which were distributed among the 19 rooms then open. The public also had the opportunity to discover two prestigious monuments: the Gallo-Roman baths and the medieval house of Jacques d'Amboise.

The appointment of Edmond Du Sommerard as head of this vast complex was to prove a wise decision, for at his death in 1885, after a directorship of forty years, he left behind a catalogue totalling 10,351 items. It is he who should be considered as the museum's true creator. His initial task was to put his father's collections into order; in his first catalogue published in 1847, he adopted a system of classification based on the different types of arts and crafts. Within each category, objects were listed in chronological order; the collector had made way once and for all for the scientist. He then undertook the reorganisation of the rooms, which until the Second World War would retain aspects reminiscent of their XIXth-century origins, and also managed to set up the Museum of National Antiquities whose creation had been so fervently desired.

Operating under the authority of the Commission des Monuments Historiques, he was able to acquire numerous architectural and sculptural fragments from restoration projects (the *Apostles* from the Sainte-Chapelle) and demolitions (the chapel of the College of Cluny). The stonework collection was completed with plaster casts, thus forming a first version of the future museum of comparative sculpture, which has since been given the old name of Musée des Monuments Français. He extended the exhibition area to the garden recently commissioned by Napoleon III, arranging architectural elements, sculptures and plaster casts under the newly-planted trees. The famous Elysée Gardens of the former Musée des Monuments Français thus made a timid reappearance. His indefatigable activity as a curator also included making purchases. He kept a watchful eye on the antiques market, never losing an opportunity to enrich the museum, which may thank him for the acquisition of some of its greatest masterpieces. In Rouen, he bought the six tapestries of *La Vie Seigneuriale* (*The Manorial Life*), after having acquired in Genoa the ten Brussels hangings of the

History of David series (today in the Musée de la Renaissance at Ecouen), which are unequalled in their size and beauty in any other museum in France. When the Hôtel-Dieu of Auxerre decided to sell the tapestries from the cathedral, he immediately persuaded the Commission and the Ministry to acquire them for Cluny. He also negotiated with the township of Boussac for the purchase of the prestigious series of *The Lady with the Unicorn*. As for silver and goldwork, he enriched the museum with several unique pieces: the gold crowns of the Visigothic kings, found by a French officer living in Spain, the distinguished remnants from the treasury of the Cathedral of Basel, the altar given by Emperor Henry II and the golden rose, sold by the canton to a private collector. His acquisitions in other domains were no less remarkable: six monumental sculpted fireplaces, three large Della Robbia ceramic medallions (today at Ecouen), paintings, enamelwork and even a collection of illustrated lead medallions found in the Seine.

His successor, Alfred Darcel, concerned himself primarily with rectifying the collections, removing imitations, dismantling composite pieces of furniture, an initiative his predecessor had not dared to take, out of respect for his father's memory.

In 1907, the Museum was detached from the Commission des Monuments Historiques and came under the authority of the Administration des Musées Nationaux. The directorship was given to Edmond Haraucourt, a poet and man of letters, whose principal accomplishment was to increase the number of works in the catalogue by removing them from the storage places to which they had been relegated.

After him, Jean-Joseph Marquet de Vasselot undertook a huge reorganisation programme, excluding many items that were out of place, and exhibiting others more in keeping with contemporary taste.

The closing of the Musée de Cluny in 1939 marked the end of an era, that of a XIXth-century museum whose life had spanned almost a hundred years. A new existence was to begin with the end of the war.

The exhibits had been transferred to a safe place during the war. With the return of peace, there was much architectural work to be done and a new presentation of the collections to be designed. The needs of the visitors, who had long suffered from overcrowded displays in restricted premises, had to be taken into account. It was therefore decided that ancient sculptures would be exhibited in the Gallo-Roman baths, and medieval works in the XVth-century house.

The collections of astonishing variety had to be adapted to buildings whose own qualities demanded respect. Thus the room of the *Thermae*, the finest example of ancient civilisation on French soil, had to be presented for itself. So as not to detract from the striking beauty of its dimension, the exhibits were limited to a few sculptures found in Paris and of the same period. The same applied to the chapel, a precious relic of the dying stages of late Gothic architecture in Paris. The collections themselves were dispersed among the twenty-four room

The Museum today

Renewed public interest in the Middle Ages, the size and diversity of the collections and the need to safeguard the ruined parts of the baths impose a new stage in the development of the Museum. This consists in protecting the Roman architecture in order to ensure its survival. The space thus gained will be used to install an entrance on the boulevard Saint-Michel, to present the collections held in reserve - the Parisian stonework deposit, fabrics, tapestries - and to open new archeological and technical sectors. The Musée National du Moyen Age will thus meet public expectations, by providing information on the Middle Ages in France and Europe, with works displayed according to an updated museological concept, and a museum circuit that is better adapted to the two buildings and the collections.

*A*rts

Illumination, frescoes, stained glass, painting

The arts of colour include such apparently unrelated fields as illuminated lettering, the great cycles of mural painting and painting of movable panels destined for domestic or religious use. The common factor lies in the colouring of a composition that is generally drawn on a flat support. Stained-glass windows may seem different, since their execution involves three techniques: painting of course, in the application of grisaille on the glass and its retouching after passing through the kiln, firing, to fix the drawing on the glass, and finally metalworking, in the leading and installation by means of saddle-bars.

The creation of a stained-glass window, like a mural painting or a tapestry, is comprised of different stages which may be executed by a painter (**21**): possibly a maquette, and above all the cartoon, a scale drawing traced on a table, then transferred onto parchment or paper, to be used as a guide by the master in stained glass. All these operations require a rational approach to work and a rigorous distribution of material tasks, in the choice and preparation of colours (of mineral, vegetable or animal derivation), of the support (wall, panel or

# of colour

parchment), the transfer of the cartoon, sometimes done by pouncing, in the actual execution of the work and its finishing.

The size alone of certain projects (**8**) justified an organisation of this kind. But it was little different when the production was meant for exportation, or at least widespread distribution, as in the case of *scriptoria*, those copying and painting workshops found in monasteries (**2**), or specialised firms, near the universities in particular, or even the great masters in stained glass of the Late Middle Ages, like Peter Hammel in Strasbourg (**22**).

Painting on panels was practised by artists who, should the occasion arise, could also work as illuminators or cartoonists. Prior to the XIVth century, the art of painting on panels was limited, but the end of the Middle Ages saw a substantial development. The invention of oil paint - said to have been discovered by the Flemish, while other artists, especially in Italy, continued to paint in *tempera*, where pigments are mixed with an egg-based medium - is fundamental to the evolution of art in the Late Middle Ages.

Dany Sandron

Arts of colour

1 Monks Witnessing the Death of St. Benedict

Ile-de-France, pre-1144
Stained glass
H 60 cm; W 38 cm
Saint-Denis , abbey church
Acq. 1958; Cl. 22758

The vertically-running inscription identifies the two monks as witnesses of St. Benedict's ascent to heaven. This scene was set in a circular medallion, part of whose border may be recognised in our panel. It no doubt came from the top of a window dedicated to the life of the saint, one of the great figures of Western monkhood, and was naturally located in the apse of the Saint-Denis abbey church, a member of the Benedictine order.

Very different in style from the other stained-glass windows from Saint-Denis, being closer to the art of illumination practised in the north of France (Saint-Bertin at Saint-Omer), this panel testifies to the diverse origins of the artists working on the abbey's reconstruction, commissioned by Abbot Suger between 1122 and 1150. It provides precious evidence of this vast project, conceived with the highest aspirations and in which the stained-glass window held pride of place. It conferred a greater spiritual dimension on the work by creating light effects infused with strong religious symbolism.

2 Virgin and Child

Rhineland, XIIth century
Illumination
H 15 cm; W 10 cm
Anonymous gift, 1885; Cl. 11308

This page was detached from a manuscript whose nature remains elusive. The theme of the Virgin and Child isolated from all context was a medieval invention that spread rapidly from the XIIth century onwards, largely due to the Cistercians who were particularly attached to the cult of the Virgin Mary.

While Gothic art underlined the maternal element in the representation of the Virgin, Romanesque art highlighted the majestic side of the character who symbolised the Church, the house of God. The formal treatment of the illuminating, with figures and decor heavily outlined and flat areas of colour, is not intended to portray reality. On the contrary, in compliance with Christianised Platonic aesthetics, it aims at evoking the essence of the subject, depicted here with a startling economy of means.

3 St. Timothy

Alsace, mid-XIIth century
Stained glass
H 58 cm; W 45cm
St. Sebastian Chapel in the Church of St. Peter and St. Paul at Neuwiller-les-Saverne
Gift of Boeswilwald, inv. in 1897;
Cl. 13335

Timothy was St. Paul's favourite disciple and Bishop of Ephesus. The palm of martyrdom alludes to the torment of his eventual stoning to death. Originally a full-length view of the saint, only the upper part of the figure remains today. The star-

2

3

more refined treatment diverges from the monumentality of these illustrious predecessors. On the other hand, its glowing colours and quite abundant use of white glass distinguish it from what was found in Alsace or Germany after 1150, when the Rhineland glassworks produced their numerous masterpieces, like the panels by Master Gerlachus (Münster Museum, Westphalia) and, at the end of the century, the great Strasbourg series.

4   **The Charity of St. Nicholas**

Troyes, St. Peter's Cathedral,
late XIIth century
Stained glass
H 45 cm; W 56 cm
Bacri Collection
Acq. 1969; Cl. 22849

shaped repair leads on the face impair one's appreciation of this figure, which seems unusual for its period. The saint's hieratic pose recalls the great prophets of Augsbourg Cathedral (circa 1100), but its

On the right of the scene, St. Nicholas is depicted secretly sliding a purse through a small opening in the wall, to bestow a dowry upon an old man's three daughters whose poverty would otherwise have condemned them to prostitution. This was an extremely well-known story in the Middle Ages. The panel was part of a

4

Arts of colour

5

series (today in the Musée de Cluny and the Victoria and Albert Museum, London) discovered in the Cathedral of Troyes at the beginning of the XIXth century. The figurative scenes and the thin inner border are typical of the style current in the southern Champagne region at the end of the XIIth century and which is also found in certain illuminated manuscripts from this area. This series could have been the work of the same artist, and is strongly influenced by art forms of the Meuse region. The outer border is from a later period and may indicate that these panels were remounted in the Gothic Cathedral of Troyes, whose construction dates from the early XIIIth century.

5   **Offering of a Church to a Saint**

Burgundy, late XIIth century
Mural painting
H 50 cm
Abbey of Charlieu refectory
Assigned in 1844, inv. in 1953; Cl. 22601

Romanesque architecture lent itself particularly well to the representation of vast painted cycles that covered large extents of bare walls. At the end of the XIIth century, the refectory of the Burgundy monastery of Charlieu was thus decorated with a mural depicting Christ flanked by evangelic symbols and enthroned in glory above the apostles and prophets, together with the abbey's patron saints and protectors. This decor was lost with the building in the XIXth century, but a few fragments were deposited at the Musée de Cluny. Among them was this crowned figure offering a church to a saint. It has been interpreted as a reference to the donations given in 879 by King Boson to the new monastery, represented by one of its patron saints, St. Stephen or St. Fortunatus, a disciple of St. Irenee, martyrised in the IIIrd. century. The frescoes are stylistically close to those of Montmorillon, in the centre of France, which also testify to the late XIIth-century revival of Byzantine influence and to the first fruits of Gothic painting, in their search for psychological characterisation of the figures.

6   **The Resurrection of the Dead**

Paris region, circa 1200
Stained glass
Diam. 58 cm
Sainte-Chapelle; D.S. 1893

The medallion was no doubt originally part of a larger composition of the Last Judgment, perhaps a rose window, in which this was a frequent, early XIIIth-century theme, as at Donnemarie-en-Montois, Chartres Cathedral or Mantes. In style and technique, it is close to the stained-glass windows of the late XIIth and early XIIIth centuries, with the same damasked background as in the Cathedrals of Troyes, Bourges and Canterbury, and its figures graced with the same classical elegance as found in Laon and Sens Cathedrals.

Like all the stained-glass windows from the Sainte-Chapelle, this panel was transferred to the Musée de Cluny during the XIXth-century restoration project, but indisputably came from an earlier building in the Paris region. It was used as a stopgap in

the Sainte-Chapelle, probably in 1765, during work undertaken by the master glazier Guillaume Brice, who did the same thing with the southern rose window in Notre-Dame de Paris.

7   **Jesse Tree (upper part)**

Paris region, 1215-1220
Stained glass
H 92 cm; W 60 cm
Former Church of Gercy (now Varennes-Jarcy, Essonne)
Historical Monuments Deposit, 1950

Christ, surrounded by seven doves, above the Virgin Mary, represented between two prophets, forms the upper part of a Jesse tree. This type of composition, elaborated around 1144 in Saint-Denis, extolled Christ's royal genealogy, starting from his ancestor Jesse and climbing in successive branches to the top of the window.

It is thought that this and other panels in the Museum (scenes from the Life of Christ and the Life of St. Martin), came

6

7

from the former church of Gercy, no longer in existence. This church must have been built at the beginning of the XIIIth century, but was transformed into an abbey in 1269, after a princely endowment from Louis IX's brother, Alphonse de Poitiers, and his wife, Jeanne (**160**). The building's change in status probably led to the early XIIIth-century stained-glass windows being transferred to the new parish church, constructed at nearby Varennes, and where the panels were found at the end of the XIXth century. In the series of stained-glass windows executed in the Paris region in the first half of the XIIIth century, these panels precede those from the refectory of Saint-Germain-des-Prés and from the Sainte-Chapelle.

8

8   Samson and the Lion

>   Sainte-Chapelle, 1243-1248
>   Stained glass
>   Diam. 59 cm
>   Sainte-Chapelle; D.S. 1895

This medallion (Book of Judges, 14:5-6), like others illustrating episodes from the life of Samson, comes from the fifth north window in the Sainte-Chapelle. This window was part of a vast stained-glass project commissioned by Louis IX to decorate the huge architectural shrine, in which scenes from the Old Testament cover almost all the great windows leading to the apse.
It has been calculated that the glasswork must have taken twenty workmen four years to complete. Three distinct workshops can be discerned from the style in this immense production of predominantly deep blue and red stained glass, so characteristic of the XIIIth century. The Samson panel belonged to the "principal" workshop, which executed the windows on

the northern side of the nave and in the apse. Its unmistakable style is shown in the softness of the drapery, the orderly compositions and the singular treatment of the trees (artichoke-shaped) and architecture.

9   St. Peter

>   Normandy, circa 1270
>   Stained glass
>   H 70 cm; W 56 cm
>   Rouen, chapel of the royal castle (?)
>   Acq. 1956; Cl. 22727

St. Peter, identified by an inscription and a key, is seated sideways on a throne whose uprights are topped by lion's heads. The museum possesses three other similar compositions of figures of apostles. The series is said to have come from one of the chapels in Philippe Auguste's royal castle, which was most likely built or decorated under Louis IX (also known as Saint-Louis). The castle was destroyed in the

XVIIth century, but some of the windows were reused in a chapel of an Ursuline convent erected on the same site, before appearing on the art market.

Together with the stained-glass windows from Rouen Cathedral (Chapel of Saint-Jean-Jouxte-les-Fonts, circa 1266, where the lancets are filled with figurative panels unframed by architecture and panels treated in grisaille), and from Evreux Cathedral (lower-south side of the nave), these panels demonstrate the trends that appeared in Normandy around 1260-1270: slenderized silhouettes, easily distinguishable compositions with sharp, bold outlines, and a lightening of the palette.

10   Decorative grisaille

Saint-Denis, circa 1324
Stained glass
H 60 cm; W 38 cm
Saint-Denis, Saint-Louis Chapel
Gift of A. Proye, 1886; Cl. 11473

This decorative panel, whose original panes have been remounted, is composed of ornamental foliage in grisaille bearing wild roses, buds and fleurs-de-lys tinted with silver stain, a chloride or silver salt-based glaze developed around 1300 that turns yellow when fired and modifies the tone of the underlying coloured glass.

For a long time thought to have come from the glasswork in the chapels in the apse of Notre-Dame de Paris, this and other simi-

9

10

11

lar panels (Dépôt des Monuments Historiques at Champs-sur-Marne; Victoria and
Albert Museum, London; Cloisters, New
York) have recently been attributed, on the
strength of XIXth drawings, to the decor of
the Saint-Louis Chapel built between 1320
and 1324 on the northern side of the nave
in the abbey church of Saint-Denis.

11 **Crucifixion and decorative
panels**

Upper Rhineland, first half of the
XIVth century
Stained glass
H 170 cm; W 105 cm
Colmar, Church of the Franciscans
Gift of Mme Montreuil, 1899; Cl. 13747

The presence of a friar wearing a Franciscan habit, tied at the waist with a knotted
cord, hence the name Cordeliers, supports
the theory that these stained-glass windows

come from the Franciscan Church in Colmar that was rebuilt between 1292 and the mid-XIVth century. These narrow panels were superposed to fill the tall church windows. The vivid chromatic range of the richly-coloured panes (lime green, blue, red and yellow), and the repeated floral motifs, especially roses and maple leaves, surrounding the figurative scenes are characteristic of stained-glass windows found in the mendicant orders of the southern Empire.

The Franciscan panels of Colmar, like those of the Dominicans in the same town, which are still in place, may be compared to the windows of the Franciscans of Regensburg.

12 Crucifixion

Auvergne, second quarter of the
XIVth century
Paint on wood
H 145 cm; W 122 cm
Sauvagnat (Puy-de-Dôme)
Acq. 1861; Cl. 3413

One of the most current themes in medieval iconography was the Crucifixion that rapidly evolved towards increasingly dramatic representations in the Gothic period. These expressive trends were conveyed more strongly in the figure of Christ than in those of the Virgin or St. John, whose pain was revealed by gestures of lamentation. Christ is depicted with arms stretched obliquely under the weight of his sagging, dead body, with legs folded and both feet pierced by a single nail on the narrow

12

13

wood of the cross. Two angels holding the sun and the moon can be seen emerging from stylised storm clouds.

The sinuous, flattened folds of the drapery date this panel from c. 1325-1350, while its singular lancet arch shape indicates that it may have come from the top of a larger composition, probably an altarpiece or a jube.

13   Antependium: scenes from the life of the Virgin

England, Suffolk, circa 1335
Paint on wood (oak)
H 94 cm; W 302 cm
Thetford Church, England (?)
Acq. 1864; Cl. 7726

This altar front, truncated on the left, is devoted to the Life of the Virgin (the Nativity, Death of the Virgin, Adoration of the Magi, Education of the Virgin). It complements an altarpiece preserved in England, in the church at Thornham Parva (Suffolk), which presents the same style and decorative technique, and features, on either side of the Crucifixion, saints mainly from the order of preaching friars. We may deduce from this particular iconography and the

Virgin's predominant role that both works were used to adorn the high altar of a Dominican church, perhaps in Thetford, not far from where the altarpiece is preserved today. Such an ensemble is most rare, considering the almost total disappearance of medieval, ecclesiastical furniture in northern Europe. As for the style, with no known, exact equivalent, it can be compared to paintings in the church of Brent Eleigh (Suffolk) which date from around 1330.

14   Two donators, Jean de Saint-Gilles and Jeanne de Tilly

Brittany, circa 1400
Stained glass
H 44 cm; W 49 cm
Betton (Ille-et-Vilaine)
Acq. 1877; Cl. 9549

Ten panels from the triple-lanceted, apsidal window have survived the demolition (circa 1870) of the church of Betton. Scenes of the Passion must have occupied the two upper registers (Calvary, Flagellation, Resurrection, Judas' Kiss, together with the missing scenes of Jesus on the Mount of Olives and Jesus before Pilate). Six panels

of donators were placed in the three lower registers, on either side of their patron saints (St. Martin [the only one remaining], St. John the Baptist, St. Apollinia or Anastasia), who were set in the central lancet. The weakly-modelled figures on colourless glass stand out against the backgrounds of bright red, blue and emerald green. The architectural decor is enhanced with silver stain. All the donators belonged to the Saint-Gilles family, who, as lords of Betton, were responsible for the upkeep of the choir. Only one woman, Jeanne de Tilly, could be identified through her coat of arms, *azur semé de fleurs de lys d'argent et d'or à une fleur de lys de gueule*, which indicates a dating prior to 1435, the year her husband died.

14

15 **Page from Gérard de Montaigu's breviary**

Paris, circa 1410-1420
Illumination on parchment
H 36 cm; W 26 cm
Anonymous gift, 1885; Cl. 11315

God the Father, wearing a triple crown, sits enthroned on a rainbow, in a mandorla topped by a canopy, surrounded by the four Evangelists and their emblems, the eagle of St. John, the ox of St. Luke, the angel of St. Matthew and the lion of St. Mark. This full-page illumination has been detached from the breviary of Gérard de Montaigu (Paris, Bibliothèque de l'Arsenal), who was Bishop of Paris from 1410-1420. His coat of arms features on the illumination of the Crucifixion, and he may be seen kneeling at the foot of the cross. The brilliant style of these two illuminations follows in the wake of the master of Bedford, one of the great Parisian artists at the start of the XVth century. The highly-coloured, chequered background is typical of XIVth and early XVth-century illumination.

Master of San Michele in Murano

16 **The Holy House of Loretto**

Lombardy, circa 1420
Illumination
H 21 cm; W 12cm
D.S. 1811, inv. in 1954; Cl. 22712

The decoarative initial letter on the parchment from a manuscript, perhaps an antiphonary, given the presence of musical notations on the back, depicts the house of the Virgin who, having left Bethlehem, sailed across the sea to Loretto, near Ancona, on the Adriatic. The earliest accounts of this miracle date from just after the fall of St. John of Acre, in 1291, and seem to want to compensate for the Crusaders' expulsion from the Holy Land, by narrating this miraculous transfer onto Christian soil of one of the important places in the Life of Christ.

15

16

17 (detail)

The miniature is attributed to the master of San Michele in Murano, a Lombard artist influenced by Emilian painting (Giovanni da Modena), who practised in the Venetian region, hence his customary name taken from a series of miniatures from the Camaldolese convent on the isle of Murano. His opulent style and frequent use of gold belongs to the Italian Late Gothic period c. 1400-1425, represented by the sumptuous works of Gentile da Fabriano and Michelino da Besozzo.

17   Table

> Northern Germany, early XVth century
> Painted wood
> L 455 cm; H 76 cm
> Acq. 1864; Cl. 7725

This long, narrow, entirely painted table was supported on trestles and no doubt used for meetings. It was perhaps painted for an official assembly attended by the holders of the arms emblazoned on the external border. In its centre, four quatrefoiled medallions separated by crests and depicting figurative scenes stand out against the green background. In the rather complex, iconographical design, at the ends of the table, stupidity (1st medallion: the parable of stupidity crowning the ass) is set opposite wisdom (4th medallion: the Judgement of Solomon), while, in the centre, the limits of power (2nd medallion: the king sitting enthroned, surrounded by an eagle, a serpent and a ship, symbolises the man familiar with three ways - in the air, by land and by sea - but ignores the fourth, that of man with a maid: Proverbs 30:18) are contrasted with the strength of the weak (3rd medallion: the fable of the lion and the mouse).

This table comes from northern Germany, as does another preserved at Lüneburg (Lower Saxony). From the style of the paintings, subsequent to Conrad de Soest, it can be dated early XVth century.

18 **St. Christopher**

Cologne (?), circa 1430
Stained glass
H 177 cm; W 73 cm
Oeconomos Coll.
Acq. 1958; Cl. 22759

Christopher was a giant of a man who helped people across a ford. His name, meaning "who carries Christ", was derived from the famous episode in which, while carrying a child who was in fact Christ across the river, he had the revelation of bearing a part of mankind's sins. The saint's bowed figure depicts the moment when his burden became intolerable. Numerous picturesque details - the fish in the water, the position of the Child Christ on the man's shoulders - enhance the scene's narrative element. St. Christopher was especially venerated in the XVth century and was invoked against sudden death. It was believed that the mere sight of his image ensured against dying that day. Hence his frequent representation, often large-scale, so as to be seen from afar. The panel's damasked background, the abundance of white glass and the softness

18 (detail)

19

of the drapery make it an excellent example of the International Late Gothic period, similar to stained glass from Cologne of around 1430.

19 Pietà

Provence, pre-1457
Painting
H 84 cm; W 130 cm
Tarascon, château
Louvre Deposit, 1910; Cl. 18509

A favourite subject at the end of the Middle Ages, the Pietà represents the Virgin Mary mourning over the dead body of Christ held on her knees, sometimes with St. John and Mary Magdalene, and two holy women, as here. The composition and certain details, like St. John's delicate gesture of removing the crown of thorns from Christ's head, have been taken from the astonishing *Pietà of Avignon* by Enguerrand Quarton (Louvre). Overall, the work conveys a knowledge of Flemish painting, visible in the tubular or deeply crushed folds of the drapery and in the treatment of

the faces. But the relentless light falling on the figures and the contrasted shadows reveal an artist well-versed in Provençal painting.

Acquired in Tarascon in 1910, the work was identified as a painting mentioned in the 1457 inventory of the château of this town, which stated it was kept in the bedroom of Jeanne de Laval, wife of King René.

20 The Jouvenel des Ursins family

Paris, mid-XVth century
Painted wood
H 165 cm; W 350 cm
Notre-Dame de Paris, chapel of
Saint-Rémy, given to the Musée des
Monuments Français in 1795, entered the
Louvre in 1829, Louvre Deposit;
inv. 9618

The members of the Jouvenel des Ursins family are represented standing in line: Jean Jouvenel (1360-1431), his wife Michelle de Vitry († 1456) and their eleven children, whose titles are listed, testifying

20

to the comfortable social position of their lineage, which gave them access to the highest governmental, parliamentary and ecclesiastical offices. This large panel was, according to the titles, executed between 1445 and 1449 and commissioned by the family for their chapel in Notre-Dame de Paris. It is strikingly archaic in its composition, with its frieze-like treatment of the non-individualised figures and the weakness of its modelling.

Jean Fouquet (?)

21 **Roundel**

Paris (?), circa 1450-1460
Diam. 19.5 cm
Du Sommerard
Collection; Cl. 1037a

21

Roundel was the name given to small circular one-piece stained-glass windows with a secular design. This one probably decorated the window of a layman's home. It bears the monogram LG, held by two young women wearing turbans and kneeling. The very simple composition is executed with great delicacy. The grisaille, applied in subtle glazes, is enhanced by the occasional touch of silver stain that highlights the initials and certain details in the drapery. The style is very close to that of Jean Fouquet, one of the greatest XVth-century French artists, whose work was a synthesis of Flemish and Italian art that reconciled the rigour of quattrocento composition with a psychological subtlety and poetic genius more characteristic of the North.

The almost identical treatment of this roundel and of an illumination by Jean Fouquet from Simon de Varie's Book of Hours (Malibu, J. Paul Getty Museum) suggests the painter's direct involvement in the cartoon, and even the execution, of the window. The monogram could stand for Laurent Gyrard, a high-ranking civil servant, son-in-law of Etienne Chevalier, who, moreover, himself commissioned Fouquet to decorate a manuscript by Boccaccio (Munich, Bayerische Staatsbibliothek).

Workshop of Peter Hemmel

22   Arms of the Müllenheim family

Strasbourg, circa 1460
Stained glass
H 92 cm; W 60 cm
Walbourg; Fouquiau Coll.
Acq. 1850; Cl. 1925

This heraldic panel is a magnificent representation of a red shield bearing a silver rose and a golden border, topped by a crest and a wild man's head. Set on grass, it stands out against a damasked blue background. This coat of arms belonged to the Müllenheim family and was found in the church of Walbourg in Alsace, at the bottom of one of three choir windows donated in 1461 by a member of this family. They have now been replaced by copies.
The panel's rich colours, the highly pictorial treatment of the grisaille, for the drapery and above all the flesh tints, and the

damasked background, where the motifs are left in a thick coat of black grisaille, are typical of the production from the Strasbourg workshop directed by Peter Hemmel, who exported works throughout the Empire, to Lautenbach and as far as Nuremberg.

23

Master of the View of St. Gudule

23   The Deliverance of the Prisoners

Brussels, circa 1470
Painted wood
H 80 cm; W 46 cm
Du Sommerard collection; Cl. 839

Together with a panel from the Thyssen Collection, this painting was part of a series inspired by the works of charity mentioned in the Gospel of St. Matthew, a favourite theme in XVth and XVIth-century Dutch painting. The door opened by the jailer

22

24

enables the captives, shackled hand and foot, to leave their overcrowded prison. The presence of Christ among the freed prisoners complies with his words, "Inasmuch as ye have done it unto one of the least of these my brethren, ye have done it unto me" (Matthew 25:40). The author of this act of mercy is the figure on the left, who some have identified as an influential personality at the court of the Dukes of Burgundy.

From its style, the panel has been attributed to the Master of the View of St. Gudule, an artist based in Brussels after 1460, and who owes his name to his numerous paintings that feature St. Gudule Cathedral. His works are distinguished by a realism that is occasionally caricatural, quite alien to the Flemish tradition then dominated by the more inspired style of Rogier Van der Weyden.

24 Episode of the flowering rod

Northern France (?) 1475-1500
Painted wood (pine)
H 100 cm; W 90 cm
Du Sommerard collection; Cl. 827

This is a painted side panel of an altarpiece whose centre panel is missing, but since the recent rediscovery of its other side panel a reconstitution of the whole piece can be suggested: the episode of the flowering rod, in which Joseph is miraculously designated as the Virgin's future husband, complements the Presentation in the Temple scene. It seems logical that the centre of the altarpiece was devoted to an important event occurring between these two scenes, very likely another episode from the Childhood of Christ, perhaps a Nativity. The backs of the panels are adorned with *Arma Christi*, Christ's insignia from which the complete story of the Passion may be told. This picturesque theme was especially popular at the end of the Middle Ages.

Formerly attributed to Burgundy, the panel (circa 1460) is now thought to have more northern origins, within the borders of Flanders. The painter's Nordic culture is undeniable. The importance attached to the architectural background recalls a painting by Jacques Daret (Paris, Petit Palais), a mid-XVth-century artist who trained in Tournai and worked in Arras.

The Franciscan from Korbach

25   Triptych of St. Gregory's Mass

Westphalia, end of the XVth century
Painted wood
H 100 cm; W 111 cm
Du Sommerard collection; Cl. 840

The centre panel of this triptych depicts St. Gregory's Mass, during which Christ appeared to the Pope to prove the real presence of God in the sacred host (**193**).

25

While the Mass is treated in the Germanic tradition, the side panels are of a different, more elegant style closer to Dutch painting and feature the donators. This family remains unidentified, but the presence of a Franciscan monk on the left-hand panel strengthens the parallel drawn between these panels and two triptychs kept in Korbach on which the painter, a Franciscan it so happens, can be seen and even indicates on one of them, dated 1527, that he was seventy-one years old.

26

26   Calendar from a Book of Hours

France, end of the XVth century
Illumination on parchment
H 22 cm; W 17 cm
D.S. 1820, inv. in 1954; Cl. 22715

The Books of Hours, books of prayers and services for the faithful, increased in number during the XVth century as private devotions of the laity became popular. They basically included the short service for the Virgin, psalms, litanies, suffrages and the burial service, prefaced by a calendar. Each month featured the list of days following the Roman calendar. Saint's days

27

to be especially honored were specified. The margins are adorned with the usual foliated design and plant motifs, but these pages are also decorated with signs of the zodiac and the main occupation of the month, like sheep shearing in the month of June. These small scenes from the lives of the faithful show how religious practise was a constant concern.

27 **Road to Calvary**

Paris, circa 1500
Stained glass
H 73 cm; W 41 cm
Hôtel de Cluny, chapel
Du Sommerard collection,
reinv. in 1942; Cl. 22391

This work is a very fine example of the art of Parisian stained-glass windows at the end of the Middle Ages, revealing both technical virtuosity in the flashed and engraved glass and the highly pictorial treatment of the grisaille.

The refined execution and dense composition of this panel are paralleled in the rose window of the Sainte-Chapelle that was reworked after 1485 and in the window of St. Vincent and St. Sixtus in the northern arm of the transept of Saint-Germain-l'Auxerrois. They all date from the end of the XVth century and are of Parisian origin. Two Roads to Calvary engraved on wood, attributed to Philippe Pigouchet, are less sophisticated in style than the Cluny stained-glass window, but very similar in composition.

The decor in the apse of the Cluny mansion's chapel was extremely homogeneous. The windows relating Christ's Passion and whose central scene must have been the Crucifixion, corresponded with a sculpted Entombment behind the altar (three heads still exist) that complemented the painted effigies of Marie-Salomé and Marie-Cleophas found at the entrance to the apse, dominated on the vault by God the Father amid the angels.

Master of Riofrio

28 **Altarpiece: Ordination of St. Martin**

Castile, circa 1500
Painted wood (maritime pine)
Each panel: H 166 cm; W 100 cm;
Predella: H 117 cm; W 213 cm
Acq. 1876; Cl. 9425

At the end of the Middle Ages the choirs of Spanish churches were decorated with large compositions made up of several panels set in a wooden framework that filled the back of the apse up to the vaults. As seen from the altar in the panel of the Ordination of St. Martin, this is how one should imagine the Museum's altarpiece, whose existing panels, together with those now lost, framed a central sculpture, all of which were placed above the predella featuring the twelve apostles. The upper panels depict four scenes from the life of

St. Martin - sharing the coat outside the gates of Amiens, the episcopal consecration, the miracle of St. Martin restoring a dead person to life, the death of the saint - as well as an Assumption scene, the Mass of St. Gregory (**25**) and, crowning the whole work, the Crucifixion. The paintings are attributed to the Master of Riofrio, a Castilian painter active around 1500, whose works were linked to panels from the village of Riofrio, near Avila, thus providing the origin of his name. His rather heavy style and his different sources of inspiration, both Nordic and Italian, situate him in a pivotal period, between northern Gothic art of the Late Middle Ages and the Italian Renaissance.

28

29 Coronation of Louis XII

Amiens, 1501
Painted wood
H 194 cm; W 111 cm
Amiens Cathedral
Du Sommerard collection; Cl. 822

Parallel to the painting of Louis XII's coronation, which took place in Rheims on 27 May 1498, the crowning of David is found on the other side panel, backed by a compassionate Virgin. According to early descriptions, on the back of the first panel were the arms of Jean le Caron de Bouillencourt, the collector of aids who commissioned the work in 1501 for the Confraternity of Puy d'Amiens. These two paintings were originally the side panels of an altarpiece, whose centre panel no longer exists, and which, like all the annual commissions made by the Confraternity, illustrated a line composed in honour of the Virgin. In 1501, the line chosen to glorify her was, "Holy Ampulla with royal action." Year by year, the Brotherhood of Puy's paintings enriched the interior decor of Amiens Cathedral, before changing tastes in the XVIIIth century decimated these annals of local painting then centuries old. The great paintings commissioned around 1520 may still be seen in Amiens (Musée de Picardie), and testify to the vitality and imagination of painters active in the Picard capital at the dawn of the Renaissance.

30 Virgin in front of the church of Saint-Wulfran at Abbeville

Abbeville, early XVIth century
Painted wood
H 114 cm; W 62 cm
Du Sommerard collection; Cl. 881

As in Amiens (**29**), a Confraternity of Notre-Dame existed in Abbeville. Each year, an elected leader chose a motto whose heavy rhetoric was similar to that in the verse from Amiens. On this panel, the Virgin and Child are found in front of a church, surrounded by eminent local personalities, and illustrate the line written on the scroll held by the leader of the Confra-

29

30

ternity in the foreground, "Church where
God held his residence." The church
recalls the main religious building in the
town, Saint-Wulfran, at that time under
construction and which remained unfinish-
ed. A second panel, in which the Virgin is
standing in front of a wheatfield, illustrates
the line, "Valley where grows the wheaten
viaticum."

*A*rt

Ceramics, leather, metals, furniture, moulds

While many medieval works exhibited correspond to commissions made by eminent personalities, and their iconography or style is thus marked with a certain individuality, the Middle Ages were however fully aware of the notion of an art market that was necessary for more everyday, utilitarian objects. This category of works is also found in the other chapters on specific techniques, with, for example, "Limoges ware" in Precious Arts (**91**), the Books of Hours in Arts of Colour (**26**) and the Nottingham alabasters in Sculpture (**184**). But, a large output, indeed a mass-production, was even more necessary to provide, at moderate prices, pottery for the common table, furniture, minor liturgical utensils, popular devotional objects or trinkets required by fashion. Nevertheless, in this section we shall also find costly works, such as Hispano-Moresque ceramics or a folding-table (**64**).

Given its intended purpose, ceramics *a priori* fitted the description of "industrial art." Ceramists, using both the wheel and moulds, supplied a huge quantity of pots and tiles, as proved by the occasional kiln found intact on archeological digs. But, the Hispano-Moresque production of the Late Middle Ages, besides being prolific, aimed at a more select clientele, as indicated by the numerous coats of arms represented (**58**). Similarly, the art of furniture reveals, in joining techniques, the need to meet the growing demand for furniture at the end of the period. But adapting a decor, with complex figurative scenes, or, at least, plant or armorial motifs, had to satisfy the buyer's individual demand.

and artefacts

Metals were worked by stamping and forging, sometimes die stamping, and their malleability either facilitated or complicated the process; it also made casting in a mould possible, enabling several copies of the same model to be produced. Iron and copperwork were associated with the former. In the Middle Ages, the casting of molten metal could only be accomplished with the most fusible metals, tin or lead, or with alloys of copper and tin (bronze) or copper and zinc (brass). Forging, stamping and embossing were done by traditional blacksmiths, while the creation of dies and moulds allied other metal-workers to their fellow goldsmiths and engravers.

An alloy of molten tin and lead was used in moulds for badges and brooches (**46**). Dies for seals (**40**) and leather (**35**) were stamped upon a malleable material (wax, lead, hide) to imprint the engraved design, a technique linked to stamping fabric, then paper, which, in the Late Middle Ages, gave rise to xylography, or woodcuts, and finally modern printing. The moulds for sacred wafers (**38**), for gingerbread and marzipan (**63**) could be categorized as midway between casting and stamping. At the end of the medieval period, the outstanding role amid all these techniques went to the engravers, who provided models for other craftsmen.

This gradual schism between the artist who created the design and the craftsman who executed it, beyond all probability at the beginning of our period, was decisive, for it formed the basis of the modern concept of the supremacy of "major" arts over the so-called applied arts.

Pierre-Yves Le Pogam

31

31   **Censer or perfume-brazier**

Eastern Mediterranean (?),
Vth-VIIth century (?)
Bronze
H 22 cm
Acq. 1893; Cl. 13086

From the Vth century onwards, Christians used incense and other aromatics for fune-

The widespread distribution of these censers, probably of Eastern origin and found from Morocco to Palestine via Egypt or Dalmatia, together with their bronze medium, indicate they were objects of current use.

32   **Crucifix**

France or Upper Rhine,
mid-XIIth century
Bronze
H 25 cm; W 19 cm
Wasset Coll.
Wasset Legacy, 1906; Cl. 14804

This crucifix with a fine green patina presents a stylised Christ on a plain cross. The same engraving is used to render the locks of hair falling on the shoulders and the folds in the *perizonium* (the cloth knotted around the hips). Under Christ's feet, the *suppedaneum* (the piece of wood supporting the agonizing body) adopts a vaguely plant-like form, perhaps recalling the legendary fabrication of the cross from the wood of the Tree of Life. With this strong schematization, the work possesses an

ral rites and later to perfume and magnify their prayer meetings, copying pagan custom. The liturgical use of this object is confirmed by the dome-like aspect of its lid, with horseshoe arcature and cruciform openings through which the smoke passed, as well as a large Greek cross topped by a dove. The utensil could be swung by means of its small chain or stood on its three feet.

32

33

Pilgrim's flask: martyrdom and miracles of Thomas Becket

England, early XIIIth century
Lead/tin
H 9.7 cm; W 8 cm
Gift of Victor Gay, 1910; Cl.18063

The Archbishop of Canterbury, whose assassination in 1170 was instigated by King Henry II of England, was canonised in 1173 (**89**). In addition to enamelled reliquaries, ampullas, or flasks, in which pilgrims took home a little miraculous water from the martyr's tomb, provide evidence of the cult that rapidly grew up around his relics. This flask was found when the Seine was dredged, which shows the widespread use of this kind of object; it is one of the

incredible vigour reminiscent of the large models in wood and metal that must have inspired Romanesque bronzesmiths.

33 **Candlestand**

Germany (Cologne region), second half of XIIth century
Bronze H 14 cm
Du Sommerard collection; Cl. 1002

In the Romanesque period, liturgical furnishings did not only include objects in precious metals. Apart from the chalice and paten, the Church left the choice of material for the various ecclesiastical articles up to each community, dependent, of course, on their resources. Cross stands and candlesticks, in particular, were frequently cast in bronze, the technique of which underwent a revival during the Carolingian Renaissance and above all from the year 1000 onwards. The body of this candlestand features three lion-paws under three dragons with heads recoiled, alternating with three other animal heads; cascades of foliated scrolls gush from their mouths. Three other dragons clasp the edge of the tray above, illustrating Romanesque artists' taste for depicting and combining monstrous creatures and spiralling plant motifs.

34

oldest examples of this series. It was large enough to depict, on one side, episodes from his martyrdom, and on the other, scenes of miracles that occurred near his tomb, together with an inscription praising the new saint's marvellous abilities.

35

35 Stamping die

France, first half of XIIIth century
Stone (schist)
Diam. 33 cm
Gift of Victor Gay, 1909; Cl. 17722

Rather schematic personifications of the twelve months of the year are found on one side of the die, with decorative motifs on the back. Dies of this sort were used for stamping leather objects that were then painted or sometimes gilded. Such objects were intended for everyday use: manuscript bindings, caskets, cases, pilgrims' bags, purses etc. They may also have served as a matrix for embossing metal that adorned boxes put to secular use.

36 Half-pound weight

Toulouse, post-1239
Bronze
Diam. 5 cm
Acq. 1849; Cl. 1782

In the Middle Ages, weights and measures played an essential part in economic life, especially as the West had no uniform system of measurement or currency. A kind of "money-shaped" weight, with an obverse and reverse, a legend and symbol, like any coin, appeared in Toulouse in the second quarter of the XIIIth century. The 1239 issue, under the principate of Raymond VII, the last independant Count of Toulouse, consisted of one-pound weights

36

Art and artefacts

about 400 gm), its multiples (up to 4 lbs) and its sub-multiples. Cast in dies probably reused until the following issue of 1400, these bronze weights bear a castle (the "Narbonne Château" of Toulouse) on one side, backed by a church with a tall bell-tower (Saint-Sernin) on the other. Both are emblems of the town also found on its seals. From Toulouse, this kind of weight spread rapidly to nearby cities, then throughout south-west France, where townships made do with using Toulouse's emblems instead of their own.

37   **Measure for the tithe**

France, XIIIth century
Bronze
H 25 cm; Diam. 24 cm
Found near Puiseaux, Loiret; Dumesnil
Coll.
Acq. 1864; Cl. 7719

In medieval times, peasants were heavily taxed. The tithe originally corresponded to a tenth of the harvest, then to a proportion that varied considerably. Paid in kind, it was intended for the Church, but often seized by the laity. A standard recipient was therefore necessary to measure the amount of cereals due to the parish priest or local lord. This measure was found at Puiseaux, in the Orleans region, and is adorned, in three superposed registers, with a foliated scroll, a frieze of horsemen and a ring of young women holding hands. Their dresses, like the falcons carried by the horsemen, evoke the tithe-owner's noble pleasures and status.

37

38

38 Mould for sacred wafers

France, second half of XIIIth century
Iron
Diam. 26 cm
Acq. 1851; Cl. 2067

From the IXth century onwards, metal moulds were used to produce the hosts needed for the Eucharist. They were made out of two plates fitted to hinged rods shaped like tongs. Several wafers could be cooked at the same time when the plates were rectangular, as was most common, but circular plates for making one large wafer also existed. The finest moulds were engraved to produce a drawing in light relief, as here, where on one side Christ shows his wounds amid the twelve apostles, and on the other, Christ blessing is surrounded by scenes of his life.

39 Chest

Ile-de-France, circa 1300
Wood (oak)
H 96 cm; L 285 cm; W 110 cm
Gift of Augustin Lambert, 1931;
Cl. 21545

The weight of this large chest makes it one of the earliest examples of a fixed, unmov-

39

able chest. Due to its huge size, it is divided by a central partition and its otherwise unmanageable lid is in two separate parts. Its decor of applied arcades, which also existed on the sides, as can be seen from the wood staining, is similar to architectural decor with its quatrefoils, its trefoil arches and motifs that date it from around 1300.

40

40 Die for the seal of the Saint-Jacques Hospital

XIXth-century moulding; original die:
Paris, 1319-1324
Brass
Diam. 6.1 cm
Inv. in 1912; Cl. 19191

The use of a wax seal (or sometimes a lead bulla) to testify to the validity of a document or to attach proof of ownership to an object existed long before the Middle Ages. But it was then its use spread from royal chancelleries to town offices, via all sorts of secular or ecclesiastic institutions. Metal dies - mostly in bronze or brass - were engraved with an intaglio design which was stamped onto the hot wax. Specialised engravers or goldsmiths carved these matrices, whose design was sometimes created by a painter, like the one for the seal (165) of the Saint-Jacques Hospice that was supplied by the famous Parisian illuminator Jean Pucelle.

41 Aquamanile

Northern Germany (Hildesheim?), early XIVth century
Bronze
H 22 cm; W 19 cm
Du Sommerard collection; Cl. 990

In the Middle Ages, both ecclesiastical practise and the rules of hospitality often involved washing one's own or one's guests' hands, hence the name aquamanile (water for the hands) or aiguière (water recipient) given to this sort of object. Put to secular or religious use, like these outstanding gemellions (**100**), metal aquamaniles were primarily made in the Meuse region and northern Germany and came in a variety of forms. In spite of their twofold use, the iconography of their decoration tended to be secular. This ewer has the form of a human bust, with a hole above the head for filling the recipient, a spout on the forehead for pouring, and a dragon-shaped handle on the back. As seen from the hairstyle, this is the figure of a young

41

man, which matches a female bust from the Museum of Troppau (now Opava, Slovakia) whose inscription in northern German confirms the origin of the pair.

42 Coins from the treasure of Colmar

Mid-XIVth century
Silver (except one golden florin)
Treasure discovered at Colmar in 1863
Acq. 1923; Cl. 20682

The treasure found in the old Jewish quarter of Colmar consisted of jewels, costume accessories (106) and a set of three hundred and fourteen coins. It is similar to other treasure troves found in the Upper Rhine region, between Colmar and Basel, which had been buried by Jews during the persecution that followed the Great Plague of 1348-1350. When this widespread epidemic killed almost a third of the West's total population, the most irrational accusations were made against various ethnic minorities, primarily the Jews. Study of the coins from Colmar has confirmed the localisation and dating suggested by historical data. The vast majority of them are bracteates, very thin silver coins, stamped in relief on one side only, showing through in intaglio on the reverse. Almost all the workshops known to mint money were situated on the Rhine, between Lake Constance and Strasbourg, while the issues date from the 1340s.

42

43

43   Salt-cellar

France (?), XIV th century
Tin
H 4 cm; L 8.5 cm
Acq. 1847; Cl. 1661

Each side of this small hexagonal box is
adorned with quatrefoils containing busts
of Christ, St. Peter, St.Paul, a Virgin and
Child (?) and two other saints. On the outside of the lid is an Annunciation scene
signed by the artist (*Bosetus me fecit*); on
the inside is a Crucifixion scene surrounded by another inscription that may be
translated: "When you are at table, think
first of the poor; when you nourish one of
them, it is God you are nourishing, my
friend." In spite of its religious decor, this
inscription suggests it was a table utensil.
Other very similar examples are found in
Berlin, Bologna and Trieste. The latter
dates their production prior to 1370-1382,
the episcopal period of the Bishop of
Trieste whose seal is stamped in the wax
that once almost completely encircled the
object. This may infer that these artefacts
had a further religious use, perhaps as reliquaries.

44   Paving tile: a bird

Champagne, XIVth century
Red ceramic, with inlaid yellow ceramic
decor
L 11 cm; W 10.5 cm
Lejeune-Laroze Bequest, 1924; Cl. 20686

Throughout the Romanesque period,
mosaic flooring was gradually replaced by
terracotta tiling, which had the same
simple, multicoloured effect, but was
cheaper. The various techniques developed
by tile makers went hand in hand with
stylistic evolution. Monochrome techniques
typical of Cistercian floors were abandoned
around 1190-1220, and followed around
1240 by the tiles in two colours characteristic of Gothic flooring. This tile is inlaid. In
other words, the design carved in relief on
a wooden punch was deeply impressed on
the clay, and the resultant intaglio motif
was then filled with another clay before
drying and firing. It must have come from
a floor executed in Champagne at the end
of the Middle Ages. The identical motif is
found on the chapel floor in the early
XIVth-century abbey of Vauluisant
(Yonne), and in a XVth-century house in
the village of Courgenay, which depended
on the same abbey.

44

45

45 Door knocker

Germany, XIVth century
Bronze
Diam. 20 cm
Acq. 1869; Cl. 20961

This lion head still has its ring, which proves it was not simply a handle but a real door knocker. Apart from its practical function, the ring had other uses linked in particular to the churches' immunity. In fact, all one needed to do to gain the right of sanctuary, was to seize the ring in one hand and pronounce aloud the formula for requesting protection. Moreover, the use of lion heads was extremely popular, from the time of Charlemagne's palatial chapel to the end of the Gothic period, which can be explained by the Christian symbolism of this animal. It was a representation of Christ, since lion cubs were supposed to die at birth and be restored to life three days later by the warmth of their sire's breath.

46 Mould for badges

Italy (?), XIVth century
Slate
H 8.5 cm; W 4.3 cm
Acq. 1932; Cl.21590

The extensive production of pilgrims' badges and devotional objects (**47**) required a technique that was reliable, fast and lucrative. Local craftsmen who supplied famous sanctuaries with their stocks of holy images therefore used lead, mixed with tin, a medium that was inexpensive, easy to work and recyclable. The metal was cast in moulds, with the part bearing the figure to be represented in intaglio and the rest smooth (since the image was flat). These moulds had an inlet channel for the molten metal and tiny air-ducts to prevent bubbles forming in the lead. Very often the mould had different figures, or even several different figures, on each side, thus increasing production capacity. On one side of this example is an image of *Saint Voult of Lucca* (A Romanesque crucifix reputed to be a true, miraculous image of Christ) and on the other, a bulla invoking the Virgin Mary.

46

47

47

47 Badges

Lead/tin

Badge of Notre-Dame de Rocamadour

France, XIVth century
H 4.9 cm; W 2.7 cm
Found in the Seine; A. Forgeais Coll.
Acq. 1861; Cl. 4770

Rosebud

France, XIVth century (?)
Found in the Seine; A. Forgeais Coll.
Acq. 1861; Cl. 4730

Lead horseman

France, XIVth century
H 6.7 cm; W 5.1 cm
V. Gay Coll.
Gift, 1909; Cl. 17751

While pilgrims' flasks were used as early as the VIIth century to take home a little holy water or oil from famous shrines (**34**), at the end of our period, pilgrims' badges, also known as "leads", were readily manufactured in huge numbers (**46**). Tokens of piety and proof of having made the journey, these small souvenirs were pinned to pilgrims' clothes or hats and were sometimes buried with them. They also provide us with a map of the great pilgrimage sites, such as Notre-Dame de Rocamadour, whose badge is a copy of its seal. Other secular insignia consist of badges worn in support of political figures, of trinkets offered by admirers to their ladies, like this rosebud, or of children's toys, such as lead soldiers and miniature dishes.

48   Baptismal font

Northern Germany, XIVth century
Bronze
H 80.5 cm; Diam. 67 cm
Acq. 1855; Cl. 2522

This font from Embsen, near Lüneburg, in
northern Germany, was cast in an alloy
similar to the one used for bells. The basin
itself is supported by four atlantes and is
adorned with medallions depicting both
decorative (lions, eagles, fleurs-de-lys..) and
religious (Virgin and Child, Crucifixion,
etc.) themes. The two latter themes are
each presented in two different styles,
which indicates that the number of
reputedly magical images was more important than a coherent cycle. This same use
of medallions is also found on bells at the
end of the medieval period, where pilgrims' badges (**47**) are a prominent feature.
The Adoration of the Magi seen on our
font probably evokes the pilgrimage to
Cologne.

48

49

49 Lectern

Dinant, 1383
Copper alloy
H 155 cm
Tournai, church of St. Nicholas;
Stein Coll.
Acq. 1893; Cl. 13062

Lecterns were used for readings and as choir singing desks, and each place of worship had at least two. The one reserved for the most solemn readings from the Gospels was frequently decorated with an eagle that was well adapted to its role both as a symbol, representing St. John the Evangelist, and by its form, its outstretched wings holding the heavy gospel-books. This lectern, dated 1383, from the church of St. Nicholas at Tournai, is one of the oldest examples of works made in Dinant, the Flemish town that gave its name to the term "dinanderie," objects made mainly in brass, either useful, like kitchen utensils or candlesticks, or more sumptuous artefacts destined for regional churches and exported throughout Europe. Cast in several pieces in a copper alloy, the lectern is a simpler version of the renowned example executed by Jean Josès around 1370 for the church of Notre-Dame at Tongeren.

50 Casket

Netherlands, end of XIVth century
Painted and gilded leather on wood
H 12.5 cm; L 26 cm; W 18.5 cm
Acq. 1910; Cl. 17506

This casket features scenes of courtly love on the outside (one motif shows the man and the woman each holding one end of her belt), while the inside of the lid displays a Virgin and Child. This kind of casket, probably offered as an engagement present, was meant to arouse sensual curiosity, but, at the same time, sang the praises of virginity. Other caskets produced in the same Flemish workshop (stylistic parallels drawn with illuminations indicate this locality, together with Flemish inscriptions, like the one on our casket that means, "when you look at it, you will remember")

depict either love scenes or religious scenes, and sometimes, as here, a combination of them both. The high quality of these artefacts, once enhanced by their polychromy, generally better preserved on the inside, point to their success in attempting to imitate, in a less noble material, the fine XIVth-century Parisian ivory caskets.

50

50

51

51 Comb of Marguerite of Flanders

Flanders (?), circa 1400
Boxwood, silver, ivory and bone
H 15.9 cm; L 20.4 cm
Acq. 1960; Cl. 22797

The comb has two rows of different-sized teeth, separated by a wide decorative area. The latter has an openwork design of smallflowers and ribbons, while the strip across the middle and the border feature wooden marquetry inlaid with tinted-green bone and ivory. A silver lozenge is found in the centre on either side, one engraved with an M and the other with a coat of arms. These are the initial and arms of Marguerite of Flanders, who, in 1369, became Duchess of Burgundy when she

52

Art and artefacts

married Philip the Bold, and died in 1405. The comb can be quite accurately dated from the blazon and is one of the earliest specimens of this kind of artefact, numerous examples of which were found at the end of the XVth century and in the Renaissance.

52   Deep basin with rings

Valencia or Andalousia, circa 1400
Lustreware
Diam. 46 cm
Acq. 1854; Cl. 2343

At the end of the Middle Ages, Spain produced large quantities of pottery decorated with a stanniferous glaze that became iridescent on firing, otherwise known as lustreware, a technique practised in Xth-century Moslem Persia. The pieces found on excavations testify to a Spanish production in the XIIth and XIIIth centuries that is now called Hispano-Moresque. The first centres appear to have been established in Andalousia, especially in Malaga, from where the lustreware technique spread into Christian Spain, recently reconquered from the Moslems, to the Valencia area in particular. This deep basin with four rings is part of a set of four, three of which are in the museum, while the last one is in New York. They were either made in Malaga at the end of the XIVth century, or, as an early imitation of Andalousian style, in the Valencian workshops at the start of the XVth century. At all events, their superb decor and sumptuous colours remained deep-rooted in Islamic tradition, at a time when Christian iconography would gradually start to impregnate Valencian workshops (**58**).

53

53   Hallmark plaque

Rouen, 1408
Copper
H 52 cm; W 32.7 cm
Acq. 1862; Cl. 3451

From its inscription, this copper plaque was begun on Christmas Eve 1408 and is one of the earliest indications that goldsmiths' activities were controlled through the compulsory use of their hallmark, as ordered by the King of France in 1355. The one hundred and forty-five craftsmen who engraved their own names on the plaque have generally placed their hallmark between their Christian name and their surname. This hallmark is always made up of the town's mark (the Lamb of God), inscribed in a lozenge above their countermark, which may be a shield, their initial or a heraldic device (sometimes allusive as in the case of a *hure*, a boar's head, for B. Hurel). The holder of this nameplate and Rouen's official inspectors could thus use it to keep check on the work of the town's goldsmiths, by comparing the hallmarks on the pieces they were given with those engraved on the plaque by the practising craftsmen. The earliest examples of the town's hallmark date from the beginning of the XIVth century (**109**).

54 Double-sided mould: St. George and the Dragon; Frederick III as a Knight

Germany, mid-XVth century
Stone
Diam. 13.2 cm
Acq. 1852; Cl. 18776

On one side of the mould St. George may be seen struggling against the dragon to deliver the Princess of Trabzon, safe on a hill, while her parents watch the fight from their palace in the background. In the Late Middle Ages, this Christian iconography was, above all, a means of exalting the values of chivalry and courtesy. On the back is a young horseman, richly dressed and surrounded by thirteen armorial shields. He has been recently identified as Frederick III, Duke of Austria, from the House of Hapsburg, in 1424, and Emperor in 1440. In style and iconography it belongs to the entrancing refinement of the International Gothic era of the 1400s, while the quality and depth of the relief suggest it was used to cast precious metals (seal or medal matrix?).

55 Breastplate pendant

France, Xvth century
Gilded bronze, formerly enamelled
H 10.4 cm; W 4.1 cm
Victor Gay Coll.
Acq. 1909; Cl. 17553

For the medieval nobleman, the horse was both an indispensable, everyday companion (war, hunting, travel) and an ostentatious sign of rank and wealth. Horses and their equipment were extremely well looked after, as may be seen from their embroidered horsecloths (**208**) and harness ornaments. Decorative objects made of two

54

55

pieces mounted on a hinge that could jingle as the horse walked (and thus act as bells) were very popular at the end of the Middle Ages. These breastplate pendants - also called mobile annulets - could be adorned simply with decoratve motifs, like crosses or rosettes, or be a way of displaying their owner's coat of arms, as on the above-mentioned horsecloths. This small pendant bore a shield quartered with the arms of France and perhaps of Toulouse.

56   Knife bearing the arms of Philip the Good

Netherlands, 1453-1467
Champlevé enamelled copper, steel
L. 38.5 cm
Révoil Coll.
Louvre Deposit, 1936; Cl.22193

At the end of the medieval period, family coats of arms and personal devices were found on all sorts of artefacts. Besides being a sign of ownership, they were also a means of glorifying a lineage or an individual and even of affirming a political or religious message. On each side of the handle, this knife bears the arms that Philip the Good, Duke of Burgundy and Count of Flanders, gave himself in October 1430, when he claimed Limbourg and Brabant. The motto the Duke adopted in January 1430, "Aultre n'arai" ("I shall have no other") is written over the two sides. He had just created the most famous of knightly fraternities, the Order of the Golden Fleece, and this motto recalls its exclusivity. Finally, on one side of the ferrule is the Duke's personal device, a flint with sparks, while, on the other, a knotted cord unites two Es, a siglum he assumed in 1453. Incidentally, this profusion of emblems dates the knife between 1453 and 1467, the year the Duke died.

56

57 Plaque in memory of Guillaume de Hellande

Beauvais (?), 1461
Copper
H 53 cm; W 52 cm
Acq. 1948; Cl. 22442

The anguish of death and preoccupation with being saved weighed upon all men in the Late Middle Ages, even the most powerful. The Bishop of Beauvais, Guillaume de Hellande, who the previous year had commissioned a large hanging, part of which, *The Deliverance of St. Peter*, is found in the Museum (**216**), aware of his approaching death, made his will in 1461, before succumbing in 1462. Among his last wishes, he mentioned the creation of one anniversary and three weekly masses to be said in the church of the Dominican friars at Beauvais, where this plaque was to perpetuate his memory and their obligation. The prelate hoped that the Dominicans' prayers would shorten his possible stay in Purgatory. In return, they would receive a useful legacy, as indicated on the plaque: Pierre Berchère's *Dictionary* and Nicholas de Myre's *Moralities,* two essential preaching aids.

58 Winged vase

Valencia, second half of XVth century
Lustreware H 60 cm
Acq. 1863; Cl. 7647

Among the Museum's very rich collection of Hispano-Moresque pottery, this vase is outstanding. Its unusual size and original form make it a luxury artefact and exclude any banal usage. Its ostentatious aspect, enhanced by the presence of arms on the "ivy leaf" background, denotes it was commissioned by a very high-ranking person. The lion on the shield could be Florentine, as the arms on a similar vase preserved in London are definitely those of

57

58

the Medici family. A detail from the latter arms (the fleurs-de-lys that charge one of the family's traditional bulla) dates the creation of these two vases after 1465.

59 **Pavis**

Bohemia (?), mid or end of XVth century
Wood and painted leather
H 89 cm; L 60 cm
Cl. 2381

Taking their name from the town of Pavia in Italy and dating back to at least the first half of the XIIIth century, pavises were body-shields worn by infantry soldiers, in liason with the crossbowmen they protected. In the Hussite wars that split Bohemia

59

between 1420 and 1436, pavis wearers played a decisive role, borrowing both the name and the tactics from Italy, while the shield's shape came from that of western Slavonic horsemen (Lithuania and Mazovia).

Numerous pavises of this type have survived, some of which come from the armoury of Zwickau, a small town in Saxony that ordered forty from the nearby Bohemian town of Chomutov in 1441. The Museum's shield may have been one of them, as it has retained what seems to be traces of the town's arms that were painted over the original decor. In any case, the iconography tallies with a Bohemian origin, since the David and Goliath theme might

recall, for partisans of religious reformer Jan Hus, their uneven, but hopefully victorious combat against the Pope's crusaders.

60   **Game box**

> France (?), end of XVth century
> Ebony and stained walnut
> L 39.9 cm; W 24.2 cm (folded)
> Acq. 1862; Cl. 3434

The box itself has two leaves, each featuring a game on either side; but two removable sliding panels also have games on both sides. Six games are possible: a card game, *glic*, on the two exterior sides of the box; a game of fox and geese, and a game of merils (ancestor of noughts and crosses), on the two interior sides; backgammon on two sides of the removable panels, a *tourniquet* and a chessboard on the remaining sides (**164**). Some of these games appear for the first time in this game box, which, however, in spite of its exceptional dating (very few comparable objects from this period exist), was not a luxury artefact, but seems to have been destined for a comfortable middle-class family.

60

61 Inlaid chest

Northern Italy, end of XVth century
Various woods
L 115 cm; W 47 cm; H 43 cm
Acq. 1861; Cl. 3421

From 1470 to around 1520, marquetry reached its zenith in Italy. While in central Italy artists created works that rivalled painting, in northern Italy, workshops produced chests and other furniture, with a purely geometric or floral decor, using a technique of cutting minute pieces of various woods, tinted bone and ivory. However, the flower vases that adorn this chest, in their painstaking stereotomy, reflect the research done on perpsective by the great Florentine and Sienese inlayers. Formerly attributed to the Carthusian

61

62

workshops (hence the name of the decor *alla certosina*), these works may also have been executed in lay workshops.

62   Chest: courtly scenes

Northern Italy, end of XVth century
Wood (cypress?)
L. 205 cm; H 62 cm
Timbal Bequest, 1881; Cl. 20400

Like the painted chests, or *cassoni*, made in Florence, this wooden chest was doubtless put to secular use. Given as wedding presents, these chests were an essential part of the furniture and were displayed in the bedroom, as a sign of the family's wealth and culture. The figures depicted here stand out against the background. In the centre, the main scene represents elegant couples encircled by musicians, around an elaborate fountain. On the right, the God of Love seems to be uniting a couple kneeling in front of him. A border featuring hunting scenes runs all around, while in the centre of the lower border, two angels are seen holding a shield which bore the family's painted coat of arms. Specific details of its technique and the extravagant costumes point to northern Italian origin, probably the Adige region, and dates this chest from the end of the XVth century.

Hans von Reutlingen (?)

63   Mould: the Annunciation

Aachen, end of XVth century
Graphite
H 17 cm; W 12.5 cm
Dornbusch Coll.; A. de Rothschild Coll.
A. de Rothschild Bequest, 1901;
Cl. 14096

Found in the XIXth century at a bakery in Aachen, together with two other moulds, *The Virgin nursing the Child* (also in the Museum) and *The Mystical Marriage of St. Catherine* (now in Berlin), this is a fine example of the marzipan and gingerbread moulds produced in large quantities in Germany in the Late Middle Ages. The cakes made in them, mostly in nunneries, were distributed at Easter and Christmas. The one depicting St. Catherine is dated 1493, which confirms our end-of-XVth-century dating, based on style. The choice of a very hard material, graphite, also used by goldsmiths to test their tools, has led to these works being attributed to a well-known Aachen goldsmith, Hans von Reutlingen. The engraved patterns of these works, like those of Martin Schongauer, were a source of inspiration for Rhineland goldsmiths.

64

63

64 **Folding table**

France, circa 1480-1500
Wood (oak?)
H 75 cm; L 90.5 cm; W 79 cm
Gastaud Donation, 1959; Cl. 22795

Medieval taste had a distinct leaning towards easily-transportable furniture. Though fixed tables existed, many were simply boards placed on trestles. Their search for convenience led to this kind of collapsible table. Human figures adorn the extremities of the base that supports five pilasters, into which are fitted four open-work panels. Resting on these are two cross pieces that sustain the octagonal table top. Tenon and mortise joints and pins are used throughout; the table top is thus detachable and when removed, frees the panels and base that can then be taken apart. This fine piece of furniture, which can be dated end of the XVth century from its tracery, could thus easily accompany its owner from house to house.

65 Lock for a chest

France, end of XVth century
Wrought iron
H 22.5 cm; L 16.5 cm
Doisteau Donation, Louvre Deposit;
Cl. 22090

This lock with a hasp was probably fixed to a chest. Imitating architecture, the piece looks to some extent like a church door, flanked by St. James and another saint standing on consoles adorned with human heads, while leaf-work springs from a bust above the bay. But this superficial resemblance is contradicted by the abundant tracery covering the rest of the object and by the overall non-architectonic aspect. Three pointed shields, bearing the arms of France, France and Brittany and the Dauphin, with the one in the middle hiding the mechanism, complete the decor.

66 Chair from the chapel of the "Picardy nation"

Paris, circa 1500
Oak
H 230 cm; W 87 cm
Saint-Denis storeroom, attributed in 1890;
Cl. 199961

From the XIIIth century onwards, when Paris became one of the West's great university towns, the Masters of Arts - university teachers - used to hold meetings with colleagues from the same geographical region, both to defend their interests and to organise university life. The so-called Picardy nation used to meet in Saint-Julien-le-Pauvre, in the Latin quarter. In 1487, they had a chapel erected on their school grounds (in the rue du Fouarre, destroyed when the rue Monge was built). Consecrated in 1506, it was used for both services and meetings. The chair and adjacent wooden panels come from this chapel.

65

66

67 **Column**

France, circa 1500
Oak
Total H 214 cm
Saint-Pierre-le-Moûtier
Acq. 1890; Cl. 12121

This singular work once stood in the middle of the chapter house in the monastery of Saint-Pierre-le-Moûtier and is distinguished by its predominant heraldic decoration. An armorial shield held by an angel at the top of the column identifies the latter as a monument erected by Philippe Bouton, Burgundy parliamentary adviser and prior from 1490 until his death in 1510. This column is a reminder that, even in a place consecrated to God, self-glorification was primordial at the end of the Middle Ages.

68

68 **Casket**

Germany, circa 1500
Leather on wood
H 20.5 cm; L 27.2 cm; W 14.5 cm
Acq. 1953; Cl.22600

The decorative scenes on this embossed casket show it was put to secular use, which however remains difficult to pinpoint. Certain scenes appear to refer the theme of

67

69

love, or even virginity, as those on the front of the casket (a pair of lovers either side of the lock; a maiden with a hunted unicorn resting his legs on her knees). This would be a suitable decor for an engagement present. But the episodes depicted on the sides (Samson and the Lion; a young girl and a monster) or on the back (two men fighting; fruit-picking) fit less easily into this iconography.

69 Passion Dish

Beauvais region, 1511
Lead-glazed pottery
Diam. 37 cm
Acq. 1862; Cl. 3443

Pottery and stoneware production evolved considerably in the Beauvais region during the Late Middle Ages and the modern period. The workshops of this area not only produced useful articles, but also more elaborate works, such as a series of dishes emblazoned in relief (like one for Louis de Villiers de L'Isle-Adam, Bishop of Beauvais from 1497-1521) or adorned with religious motifs. The Passion dish is one of several such dishes in existence. Around the intertwining letters of Christ's monogram, IHS, can be seen the shield of France alternating with the letter K, the mark of Charles VIII, and then, in a second zone, instruments of the Passion alternating with various coats of arms, including that of Anne of Brittany. An inscription from *Stabat Mater* ends with the date 1511. The chronological contradiction with the dating seemingly imposed by the arms (Charles VIII died in 1498) can be explained by the fact that these dishes, however sumptuous, were probably late imitations of even more valuable goldsmiths' prototypes.

Goldsmithery and enamelling

In the Middle Ages, enamels (finely-ground coloured glass fixed to a support) were closely linked to the work of precious metals, first because they were often combined in the execution of reliquaries and instruments of worship, and thus the same craftsmen could be both silver and goldsmiths and enamellers, but the underlying reason was that enamels were considered as costly materials, like precious stones. Nor can the art of jewellers be separated from that of goldsmiths. Indeed, there was an entire production devoted to secular jewellery (especially rings), where precious stones formed the focal point of the work; but more frequently, these stones, unfaceted and merely cut in cabochon, were used to enhance works in gold or silver, by highlighting, for example, the border of a binding or the top of a reliquary.

Moreover, one should not be surprised to find all the works executed in gilded copper in this section. In the medieval period, this was not simply a substitute for more costly creations in gold and silver, commissioned by those less wealthy or more austere; very often enriched by champlevé enamels, gilded copper became, particularly in the workshops of Limoges, the ideal support for creations by "goldsmiths".

These creators remain little known, like other medieval craftsmen. Yet, perhaps because of their work with precious metals, they were not only strictly monitored, but also occasionally appointed to a prestigious rank, such as Guillaume Julien, one of Philip the Fair's Parisian goldsmiths (105). This necessary supervision soon led to a system of quality control through the use of hallmarks (109 and 53). Despite the rare number of works signed or identified by contracts, some great XIth-century goldsmiths are known,

Precious arts

such as Roger de Helmarshausen, once thought to be the monk "Theophilus", author of a famous treatise on the arts. From the XIIIth century onwards, contracts are occasional sources of information, as in the case of the reliquaries from Saint-Gertrude of Nivelles or Saint-Germain-des-Prés in Paris, but they should not always be taken at face value. Another documentary asset lies in purchasers' accounts, like those of the Papacy that recently enabled researchers to identify the creator of the *Golden Rose* of Basel as Minucchio da Siena (**107**). At the end of the Middle Ages signatures were more frequent, like that of Hans Greiff, on the statue-reliquary *St. Anne the Trinitarian*, which also bore the date of the work (**121**).

After the preliminary drawing, which was either done by the goldsmith himself or supplied by another artist, the different creative stages can be briefly summarised: fashioning and decorating the metal (embossing, engraving, chasing, stamping etc.), joining, gilding, the addition of elements such as granulations or filigree work, and the setting of stones. But medieval silver and goldsmithery is largely characterised by the addition of opaque or translucid enamels that may play either a secondary or principal role. It was during the Middle Ages that almost all the techniques possible in the domain were developed or created, from cloisonné enamelling on gold to painted enamels created in Limoges towards the middle of the XVth century, not forgetting champlevé enamelling on copper, basse-taille enamelling on silver, in the round enamelling on gold, or even "plique" enamelling, a technique invented by Parisian goldsmiths around 1300 that were masterpieces of refinement and skill.

Pierre-Yves Le Pogam

70

70   **Torque**

Gaul, IIIrd-Ist century B.C.
Gold
Max. diam. 14.5 cm; thick. 1.9 cm
Found at Soucy (Aisne) in 1866;
Louis de Cambacérès Coll.
Acq. 1866; Cl. 8071

This golden torque, found with another
slightly smaller one, is made of four strands
twisted together with unusual quadrangular
ends. First, lengthwise grooves were made
in the gold with a burin, then the rims were
decorated with a beaded motif, and finally
it was twisted when hot, then polished. It
was no doubt a votive offering (given its
shape and rigidity), and together with the
other torque tallies with the many representations of votive ornaments, associated
in particular with the god Cernunnos, who
often wore a torque around his neck and
carried another in his hand. This kind of
Celtic jewellery could be used to adorn
wooden statues of Gallic gods.

71   **Zoomorphic enamelled fibula**

Roman empire, IInd-IIIrd century
Bronze, champlevé enamel
H 5.4 cm; W 3.6 cm
Wasset Legacy, 1906; Cl. 15074

Fibulae were used in Antiquity to fasten a
garment rather like a modern-day hook,
but their role was even more important
since clothes were entirely made up of
loose material, draped in various degrees of
intricacy. This explains the very high number of existing specimens that were generally found in tombs, where the dead,
according to ancient tradition, were buried
with their clothes and other objects, at least

71

72

72

up until the VIIth century. These fibulae cover a period spanning the Roman era and the Carolingian Renaissance, and so come in a wide variety of forms and quality, from the simplest to the most elaborate. This example is seahorse-shaped (others in the collection feature a dog, an eagle or even the sole of a shoe) and was once enamelled.

72 Pair of eagle-shaped fibulae

Visigoth region, VIth century
Bronze, coloured glass-paste inlays
H 13.5 cm; W 6.6 cm
Acq. 1863; Cl. 3479-3480

Found in the Tarn-et-Garonne area, this pair of fibulae was probably of Visigothic origin. In the VIth century, the Visigoths, in addition to a large part of the Iberian peninsula, still occupied this region (Septimania, which roughly corresponds to Languedoc), despite the Frankish progression. Compared to Roman fibulae (**71**), the jewellery worn at the time of the Barbarian kingdoms displayed several novel elements. Certain techniques were fashionable, such as inlaid glass-paste or cabochons in the alveoli, formed by cloisons built up on the base plate. Furthermore, a tendancy towards stylised form, as already seen in some Roman pieces, is very apparent in this pair of fibulae, where the representation of an eagle has become more of an abstract symbol than a real likeness.

73 **Pectoral cross**

Italy (?), second half of VIth-VIIth century
Hammered, stamped gold
H 12.8 cm; W 10.9 cm
Wasset Legacy, 1906; Cl. 14964

This kind of ornament was generally made by die-stamping a sheet of gold (the same decor is found on the four limbs, while another die was used for the central motif), before cutting the cross out of the sheet. These successive operations explain why the motifs are sometimes broken off abruptly, as may be seen on this cross. Sewn on garments at chest level, as either a sumptuous or funerary ornament, these crosses were found throughout Lombard Italy and also in regions of present-day southern Germany and Switzerland. The Lombards had conquered northern Italy from the Byzantine Empire in 568, but this kind of decoration, of Mediterranean inspiration, illustrates the continuity between the Classical world and the so-called Barbarian kingdoms.

74

73

Precious arts

74 Fragment from a ceremonial sword

France, VIth-VIIth century (?)
Wood, gold, copper, niello, steel
L 29.8 cm; W (hilt guard) 8.1 cm
Acq. 1865; Cl. 7957

Found when the Seine was dredged, this sword came to us incomplete. It is made up of a damasked blade, a technique at which Frankish armourers excelled and which produced highly shock-resistant arms, and a gold-plated hilt guard. It is still in its sheath, a remarkable example of the luxury treatment Merovingian warriors gave their arms. This unique sheath is composed of gold and niello inlays on copper that, on one side, form a design of monsters and dragons within a geometric decor and, on the other, stylised griffons.

75 Liturgical sieve

Gaul, VIth century
Silver, niello, garnets
L. 17.2 cm; Diam. 4.6 cm
Acq. 1986; Cl. 23248

These sieves for straining wine or snow in particular are known to have existed as early as the ancient period. But this example's liturgical role, confirmed by the inscription, was to filter the wine into the chalice to avoid any impurity, during the Eucharist.

The inscription, in the name of bishop *Albinus*, not only implies its religious use, but can also be linked to St. Aubin, Bishop of Angers from 529 to about 550. This dating would match the presence of garnets on the handle, while the rather elegant epigraphy and the stylised dolphin motif show a certain continuity with the classical tradition of Roman silverwork.

76 Votive crown

Visigothic Spain, VIIth century
Gold, precious stones, pearls, rock crystals, glass beads
Total H 67.3 cm; Max. diam. 16.8 cm
Acq. 1859; Cl. 2879

This crown was found in 1859 at Guarrazar, not far from Toledo. Between 1858 and 1860, twenty-six crowns and diverse elements were uncovered here, many of which have since disappeared. They had obviously been hidden during the Arab invasion of 711, but doubtless came from the churches of Toledo, the capital of the Visigoth kings. The crowns are of quite different styles (the Museum's other two crowns are in latticework and openworked arcades). This one consists of a smooth golden headband, studded with precious stones and glass beads in cabochon. It is combined with a cross (as were other crowns) with a dedication by Sonnica engraved on one side. This person is other-

75

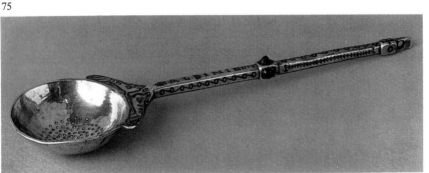

76

77 Reliquary

Western Europe, end of VIIth-VIIIth
century (?)
Silver and gilded copper on beechwood,
glass beads
H 8.2 cm; L 9.2 cm; W 2.9 cm
Acq. 1900; Cl. 13968

The reliquary resembles a small box, the lateral sides of which are adorned with a silver flower and two stones in cabochon, while the back is undecorated. The focal point is the front: the plaque of gilded silver is worked in repoussé and depicts a figurative scene that testifies to a revival of Mediterranean traditions in the abstract art of Barbarian kingdoms. Between the apostles Peter and Paul, both named and identifiable from their different tonsures, stands the Virgin holding the Child Jesus, who is apparently giving benediction. An inscription above them hails the Mother of God and Christ.

The representation may seem awkward, but the hierarchy of the holy figures is well indicated by the predominant position of the Mother and Child, which slightly masks the apostles, and by their haloes (Peter and Paul have none).

77

wise unknown, whereas other crowns were offered by famous kings like Recceswinthe. These crowns were not actually worn, as may be gathered from their size and pendants, but were probably faithful reproductions hung in the sanctuaries to express the submissiveness of earthly kingship to divine power. This practise no doubt reflected Byzantine court customs, but the multiplicity of traditional techniques evident here betrays the complexity of the "Barbarian" civilisations of the West.

QVIS SICVT HEL FORTIS MEDICVs SOTER BENEDICTVS

PROSPICE TERRIGENAS CLEMENS MEDIATOR VSIAS

78

78 Altar front from Basel Cathedral

Fulda (?), early XIth century
Gold on oak, precious and semi-precious
stones, pearls, glass beads
H 120 cm; W 177.5 cm; TH 13 cm
Treasury of Basel Cathedral
Acq. 1854; Cl. 2350

Altar fronts worked in gold were particularly numerous until the Romanesque period, but today are exceptionally rare, unlike the stone altar fronts and painted or carved altar pieces that succeeded them. They decorated the anterior face of the altar table (hence the Latin name *antependium*), as opposed to altarpieces, placed behind (*retro tabula*). Under the arcades dominated by the four cardinal virtues, the majestic figure of Christ blessing is surrounded by the three archangels and "the father of Western monks", St. Benedict. At the feet of the Saviour, in veneration, are Emperor Henry II and Empress Cunégonde (later sanctified by the Church),

minuscule in comparison with the holy figures and prostrated in an attitude of humiliation. A complex, even pedantic, inscription stresses the importance of St. Benedict and Christ the Saviour and Healer.

The Emperor certainly did not intend this work to go to Basel Cathedral; its iconography suggests it was destined for the Abbey of Michelsberg, in Bamberg, or Monte-Cassino, motherhouse of the Benedictine order.

At all events, the altar front must have been created in another artistic centre of the Germanic Empire, probably at Fulda. However, the presence of a large number of oriental artists in the Ottonian Empire (**135**) may well explain the Byzantine elements found in the figures and decor of this work. To celebrate the power of Christ and his herald, Benedict, but also, despite his apparent humble position, to glorify that of his earthly representative, the Emperor, the combined Carolingian and Byzantine sources of Ottonian art (named

79

after the Emperors Otto, Henry II's predecessors) were used to serve equally grand-
iose religious ideas and political ambition.

80

79 **Portable altar**

> Fulda (?), first third of XIth century
> Porphyry, partially gilded silver on wood
> L 25.6 cm; W 23 cm
> Frédéric Spitzer Coll.
> Acq. 1873; Cl. 13072

In the Middle Ages, both simple clerics
and great prelates were constantly on the
move. But divine services were without
intermission and had to be celebrated
everywhere; portable altars were thus used,
consecrated as an altar table and, similarly,
made in stone and containing relics, but
which could fit into a trunk or casket. This
one must have been made for a bishop of
Bamberg, for on the front may be seen,
among others, St.Peter and St. Paul (the
cathedral was dedicated to the two apostles
and to St. Kilian, whose relics were en-
closed in this altar) respectively receiving
the keys and the Law from Christ, beside
St. Blaise and St. Nicholas (whose relics
were in the cathedral). Also on the front

are representations of Melchisedec, Aaron
and Abraham announcing Christ's sacrifice
and his renewal in the celebration of the
Eucharist. On the back, the four cardinal
virtues surrounding the Lamb of God are
almost identical to those on the Basel altar
front (**78**), which is one of the elements
that establish the town of Fulda as the most
likely origin of this work.

80 **Portable altar**

> England, circa 1025-1050
> Porphyry, partially gilded silver on wood,
> niello
> L 26.1 cm; W 13.8 cm
> Maillet du Boulay Coll.; Stein Coll.
> Acq. 1886; Cl. 11459

Anglo-Saxon art reached its zenith around
the year 1000 and, far from being a reflec-
tion of Continental works, evolved in a
highly original fashion, adopting certain

trends of Carolingian art. IXth-century illuminators and ivory workers in Rheims had created a world of lively, even tormented images, incarnated in the *Psalter of Utrecht*. This found its way to England at the end of the Xth century and had a decisive influence on the island's art. But, in the Anglo-Saxon kingdoms, it was also to meet a spirit predisposed to this expressionist vision, which is conveyed here by the sunken body of Christ, the restless drapery of the Virgin and St. John, or by the wing movement of the two archangels, in total contrast to the classicism evident in contemporary Ottonian art (**78-79**). This art remains today above all in illuminated books and, to a lesser extent, in ivories; this portable altar thus represents one of the very rare examples of Anglo-Saxon goldsmithery in existence.

the gilded and nielloed figures represent the Virgin and Child of the Hodegetria type (who shows the way) encircled by scenes of the Childhood of the Virgin, taken from the apocryphal stories (Presentation of the Virgin in the Temple, in which she was then fed by an angel), of the Annunciation and the Crucifixion. There is also a portrait of the donator, a monk, Kosmas, whose name is unfortunately too common to help localise the artefact's precise origin. This work, which probably came from a church in Asia Minor, is an

81 **Cross**

Byzantium, end of XIth-XIIth century
Partially gilded silver on iron, niello
H 57.5 cm (without the tenon); W 39 cm
Acq. 1987; Cl. 23295

This work is a glorification of the Mother of God: on the front, the figures worked in repoussé and gilded depict Mary in the centre flanked by two archangels, above John the Baptist, while her Son dominates the whole scene. It is a variation of the Deisis, or the supplication of Christ by the two privileged mediators, the Virgin and the Precursor. On the back, in the centre,

81

example of a cross that was current in the Byzantine Empire, carried in processions or fixed on an altar, but which destruction has now made exceptionally rare.

82 Binding of a Gospel from Novara

Northern Italy (?), early XIIth century
Partially gilded silver on oak board, niello; parchment
H 28.3 cm; W 20.4 cm
Engel-Gros Coll.; Rütschi Coll.; Cassel Coll.
Acq. 1954; Cl. 22653

This magnificent binding with its original manuscript was destined for the Cathedral of Novara. On the front, Christ is seen handing the keys and the Law of God to Peter and Paul, framed by four other apostles; depicted underneath are five bish-ops, the apostolic successors, among whom are the famous Archbishop of Milan, St. Ambrose, with St. Eusebius, the first Bishop of Verceil, and also local saints like St. Gaudentius and St. Agabius, the first Bishops of Novara. The central position of St. Syrus, first Bishop of Pavia, attests to the importance of Pavia's role in Novara's affairs. On the back cover, the more fragmental Crucifixion scene reveals the various techniques applied to the work: under the silver plate lies the padding, a mixture of clay and wax used to sustain the figures in relief. Stylistic analysis indicates the binding was of local north Italian manufacture, with strong Germanic influence.

82

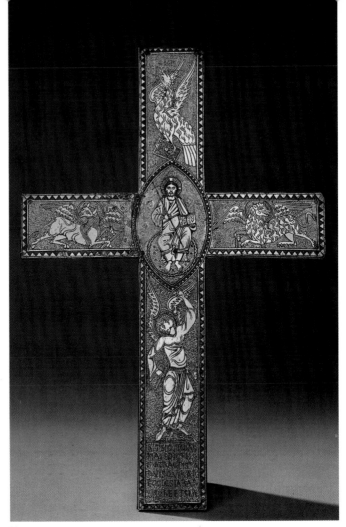

83

83 **Cross**

Italy (?), early XIIth century
Gilded copper
H 36 cm; W 45 cm
Hochon Coll.; Bac Coll.
Acq. 1895; Cl. 13229

An early XIIth-century dating can be given
to this cross, due to its similarity with one
in Princeton dated 1129, but the provenance of the group that includes crosses in
Toledo and Sienna is more difficult to pinpoint. The very high quality of the engraving, especially apparent in the figure of the
angel of St. Matthew, at the bottom of the
shaft, draws parallels with the style of
Roger de Helmarshausen, a famous Saxon
goldsmith at this time; but it could also be
of southern origin with Nordic influence.
The cross is inscribed with a curse meant
to deter possible thieves, which shows it
came from a church dedicated to St. Bar-
tholomew.

84

84 Pentecostal altarpiece

Meuse region, circa 1160-1170
Gilded copper on wood, champlevé
enamel, brown varnish
H 85 cm; L 215 cm
Seized in Koblenz during the Revolution;
deposited at Saint-Denis
Attributed to the Museum in 1895;
Cl. 13247

Whatever its original destination may have
been (Koblenz or Stavelot), this work is a
shining example of art in the Meuse region
at its peak. Beneath its apparent simplicity
- Christ blessing the Apostles, as the Holy
Spirit descends in tongues of fire, on Whit-
sunday - lies the theological subtlety displayed by the monks of the Liège region
who supervised the iconography of the
works they commissioned. Thus, the seven
columns separating the six groups of
apostles allude both to the seven columns
in the house that Wisdom built in the
bible's Book of Proverbs and to the seven
gifts of the Holy Spirit. The numerous
possible stylistic parallels (St. Héribert's
shrine at Deutz near Cologne, the apostles
on the left side of St. Servais' shrine in
Maastricht or the Evangelists on the portable altar of Stavelot) firmly establish this
altarpiece as the work of the Meuse goldsmiths.

85 The Rivers of Paradise

Meuse region, mid-XIIth century
Gilded copper
H 22.5 cm; W 15 cm
Monfort Coll. (sold under the name of
Baron Schomberg)
Du Sommerard Collection (acquired in
1836); Cl. 1362

This openwork plaque was doubtless the
back of a bookbinding, whose front cover
probably depicted Christ in Majesty sur-

85

86 Reliquary plaque: the Crucifixion

Hildesheim (Lower Saxony), circa 1160-1170
Gilded copper, champlevé enamel
H 9 cm; L 15.3 cm
Franz Engelke Coll.;
Frédéric Spitzer Coll.
Acq. 1893; Cl. 13068

While goldsmithery and enamelling developed in the Rhine-Meuse area, the most prolific northern European region in this field, other slightly different traditions existed. Lower Saxony, where the Guelphs made imperial claims against the reigning dynasty, produced a series of works of which this reliquary plaque is a fine example, together with a matching plaque in Brussels.

The silhouettes making up the Crucifixion scene stand out against the blue enamel background that is dotted with gold to add a sense of nocturnal depth. But, like his fellow craftsmen, the Meuse enameller was prone to didactic inscriptions. Here they explain the role of each holy figure - the Virgin giving birth, the Church believing, Christ dying, the Synagogue fleeing, the Disciple obeying - while, prostrate at the foot of the cross, the donor monk remains anonymous. Its Lower-Saxon origin on the grounds of style is confirmed by the fact that it belonged to a private collection at Hildesheim in the early XIXth century.

rounded by the four Evangelists. Theologians of the Romanesque era and especially Meuse scholars, like Abbot Rupert de Deutz, practised "typology", or, in other words, associated events from the New Testament with their prefigurations, or "antetypes", in the Old Testament. The four rivers of biblical paradise (the Tigris, the Euphrates, the Gyon and the Phison encircling here the Lamb of God) were thus a presage of the four Evangelists who would water the world with the message of Redemption, as confirmed in the inscription around the edge. Despite the complexity of the imposed design, the delicacy of the engraving and anatomical rendering makes this a masterpiece of Romanesque stylisation with a hint of Antiquity.

86

87

Museum's plate, Jesus, recognised from his cruciferous halo, has become the all-powerful God filling the universe. His mandorla relegates the evangelistic symbols to the corners, a framing technique typical of Romanesque art. Enthroned on a rainbow, this Christ in Majesty above all demonstrates how this art form infringes the laws of reality: the overlong tapering fingers conferring blessings, the distended abdomen and legs with billowing drapery, the vivid, contrasted colours of the enamels. All these convey the cosmic force of a God who has now conquered death, inspiring fear and trust at the same time.

87   Bookbinding plate: Christ in Majesty

Southern workshop (Limoges region or Spain?) circa 1150-1175
Gilded copper, champlevé and cloisonné enamel
H 23.6 cm; W 13.6 cm
Frédéric Spitzer Coll.
Acq. 1893; Cl. 13070

Formerly one of a pair with a *Crucifixion* plate today preserved in Madrid, this work was no doubt part of the binding for a valuable manuscript. Like all masterpieces, its origin is hard to pinpoint. While certain aspects present similarities with Spanish works (*Urna* from Silos in Burgos), it also heralds the development of Limoges enamel industry. The work in Madrid stresses the humility of a Christ of human dimension and the tragedy implied by the death of God, underlined by the violent movements of the Sun and the Moon. But, in the

88

89

88 Plaque from the high altar at Grandmont: St. Etienne de Muret and Hugo Lacerta

Limoges, circa 1190
Gilded copper, champlevé enamel
H 26 cm; W 18 cm
Du Sommerard collection; Cl. 956

Etienne de Muret was one of a group of ascetics (including Bruno de Cologne for the Chartreuse, Norbert de Xanten for Prémontré, Robert de Molesmes for Cîteaux) who, at the end of the XIth and start of the XIIth centuries, transformed Western monkhood. "Follow the naked Christ naked" was the ideal of absolute poverty preached by Etienne, the hermit who founded the Order of Grandmont in 1077. However, thanks to the success of his reform and the protection of Plantagenet King Henry II, the community of Grandmont grew rich and commissioned sumptuous ecclesiastic furniture from the nearby Limoges workshops.
The two plaques preserved in the Museum are probably the only remaining parts of the altarpiece from the high altar, doubtless executed just after the founder's canonisation in 1189. Among scenes from the life of Christ, such as the Adoration of the Magi, are episodes from the life of St. Etienne, including his posthumous apparition to his disciple Hugo Lacerta, an enigmatic scene luckily solved by the inscription in the Limousin language. These plaques were executed in the Limoges workshops at the dawn of their rising success, in a style that betrays elements borrowed from the Plantagenet domain and others that would become characteristic of the Limoges enamels.

89 Reliquary of St. Thomas à Becket

Limoges, circa 1190-1200
Gilded copper, champlevé enamel
H 15 cm; W 16.6 cm
Acq. 1987; Cl. 23296

England's Chancellor and Archbishop of Canterbury, Thomas Becket was assassinated in his cathedral during the Eucharist, on 29 December 1170. His canonisation in 1173 was the Papacy's swift reaction to this heinous crime instigated by England's King Henry II. The relics of the new martyr, who soon became popular, were rapidly distributed all over Europe. The Limoges workshops supplied a large number of stereotype, shrine-shaped reliquaries (two of the remaining fifty or so are in the Museum), whose form evolved however between 1170 and 1200.
The front, displayed to the faithful (the soberly-decorated back was not usually on view), depicts the murderers striking Becket's head, as he stands near the altar and seems to offer himself as a victim, actually renewing Christ's sacrifice. On the sloping top, the martyr's burial is represented. These images surely served ecclesiastical propaganda purposes as efficiently as chroniclers' accounts worked against the abuse of political power.

90 Reliquary

Northern France (?), circa 1200
(rock crystal plaques: Fatimid Egypt)
Gilded silver on wood, filigrees, rock
crystal, gems and pearls
H 11.3 cm; L 14.8 cm: W 9.7 cm
Treasury of the Cathedral of
Moûtiers-en-Tarentaise
Acq. 1887; Cl.11661

90

This reliquary is interesting because it demonstrates the frequent medieval practise of reworking a secular Islamic artefact and changing its purpose. Here, the plaques of rock crystal decorated with ibexes, alone or affonté, around a palmette, come from a casket created in Xth-century Fatimid Egypt. The Christian goldsmith who obtained it (through trade, as a gift or even from a returning Crusader's loot) cut them into four parts to make the sides of the reliquary, before mounting them on a gilded wooden support. The relics within the casket may be glimpsed through the transclucent rock crystal.

91 Crozier with palmetto-flower motif

Limoges, early XIIIth century
Gilded copper, champlevé enamel
H 25.5 cm; W (scroll) 12.5 cm
Found in the choir of Narbonne Cathedral
Acq. 1860; Cl. 2957

Eucharistic dove

Limoges, first third of XIIIth century
Gilded copper, champlevé enamel
H 19 cm; L 25 cm
Mallay de Clermont Coll.
Acq. 1851; Cl.1957

After the IVth Lateran Council, presided over by Innocent III, Christian Europe may be considered as fully constituted, with a solid ecclesiastical framework dominating society from parish to cathedral. The need for liturgical furnishings required for worship was thus even greater and the clergy placed a mass order for altarpieces, reliquaries, crosses, croziers, manuscript bindings, censers, candlesticks and pyxides. The Limousin workshops met this demand more than adequately, distributing throughout the West and offering a wide range of quality and prices. This mass production of "Limoges work" is not merely interesting in its emergent masterpieces, but also in what is learnt from more modest objects about the customs and mentality of a Christian society. This Eucharistic dove, a sort of mobile tabernacle that was hung over the altar on a chain, testifies to their concern for the consecrated Host, the living image of the Holy Spirit, thus placed beyond reach of defilement. The Limoges workshops also supplied bishops and abbots with their croziers (**141**), symbols of pastoral dignity that were historiated or adorned with a floral motif as here.

91

Precious arts

92

92 Reliquary from Notre-Dame de Termonde

Flanders, circa 1220-1230
Gilded silver on wood, niello, precious
stones and rock crystals
H 24.1 cm; W 13.4 cm
Frédéric Spitzer Coll.
Acq. 1893; Cl. 13073

The original six-lobed reliquary probably
had a more modest stand than it does
today; this type of reliquary was sometimes
called a phylactery. The relics could be
seen through the central filigree and openwork on the hinged front that, when opened, gave access to the precious remains,
which included a piece of wood from the
Cross. The main decorative scene on the
back is of Christ blessing, surrounded by
St. Peter and St. Paul, two other anonymous saints, the moon and perhaps the
sun. The work, which may have originally
been made for the collegiate church of
Notre-Dame de Termonde, in a centre of
minor importance, is a late example of the
great Rhineland-Meuse creations.

91

93

93 **Reliquary plaque: St. Francis receiving the stigmata**

Limoges, circa 1228
Gilded copper, champlevé enamel
H 20 cm; W 20 cm
Private Coll. (Rodez)
Acq. 1851, Louvre Deposit; L. OA D 81

This plaque comes from a quatrefoiled reliquary mounted on a stand, or phylactery (**92**); a similar, complete reliquary is found in the Louvre.

Francis of Assisi, the *Poverello*, had thrown Umbria, Italy and the whole of Christendom into confusion, by his preachings and his life itself, remaining faithful to the Church, but determined to revive it with the spirit of the Gospel. He was sanctified after his death in 1226 by popular faith and canonised by Rome two years later. The Order he had founded, in spite of himself, pledged to spread his message.

By choosing to depict the miracle of the stigmatisation (marks resembling the wounds on Christ's crucified body impressed on his flesh by a seraph), the Franciscan friars recalled that their founder, the first man to be granted such an honour, had lived like a "new Christ". Moreover, the presence of stars and trees is evidence of the possible Italian influence weilded by the Franciscan purchasers in the Limoges workshops.

94 **Cross from Bonneval**

Limoges, circa 1225-1235
Gilded copper on wood, champlevé enamel
H 43 cm; W 35.2 cm (lower part missing)
Acq. 1977; Cl. 22888

No doubt originally commissioned for the Abbey of Bonneval in Rouergue, on the front of the cross is a Crucifixion scene and on the back, a Christ in Majesty. While very characteristic of Limoges work in the 1200s (colouring, shape of the cross), a later dating would be justified by numerous figurative innovations. For the first time in Limoges enamelwork, Christ's body appears dead and collapsed, and above him, the angel with outstretched hands recalls a priest's attitude when celebrating mass. These features demonstrate interacting influences between the Limoges workshops and contemporary Italian art.

95   Great reliquary of St. Fausta

Limoges, circa 1225-1250
Gilded copper on wood, champlevé enamel, rock crystals
H 45 cm; L 52 cm; D 16 cm
Church of Ségry (Indre)
Acq. 1858; Cl. 2826

Unlike most reliquaries from Limoges (except Mozac and Gimel), the two long sides are historiated. The main side is adorned with the Crucifixion and Christ in Majesty (with overlaid figures), while on the opposing side is the story of St. Fausta's martyrdom (with reserved and engraved figures). The different, successive episodes are related, sparing nothing of the young girl's torture. The abstract background strewn with small flowers is transformed in the last scene into a hillock on which the executioner stands ready to decapitate the saint; but her final victory is ensured by the death of the executioner, struck by lightning, in the form of a symbolic arrow. The weakened colour range and the technique of engraving or overlaying figures on the enamelled background (more economical than the former reverse process) are compensated by the fluidity of the drapery.

While few representations of this obscure saint exist, the Museum also possesses another smaller, later reliquary dedicated to her.

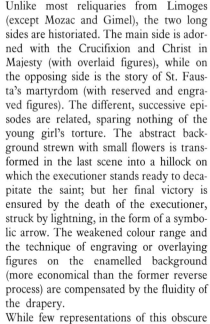

94

95 (detail)

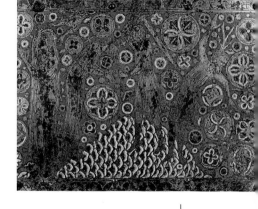

96 Openwork medallion: Grapes from the Promised Land

Limoges, circa 1225-1250
Gilded copper
Diam. 8 cm
Du Sommerard collection; Cl. 957 b

This appliqué medallion belongs to a series of four and perhaps came from a casket or tabernacle (*The Creation of Man* and *Moses Striking the Rock* also in the Museum; the fourth, *Moses and the Brazen Serpent*, in the former Martin le Roy Collection). The late influence of Rhineland-Meuse art is visible. They are the only known Limoges works on a biblical theme with explanatory inscriptions. They not only borrow this formal northern tradition - see the numerous inscriptions on the Museum's Meuse and German works (**85-86**) - but also their iconography: subjects like Grapes from the Promised land (a giant bunch of grapes brought back from Cana by Joshua that

97

symbolises Christ on the Cross) or scenes from the life of Moses were typical of the Meuse tradition.

97 Upper half of a hand-warmer: the Liberal Arts

France, circa 1230-1240
Gilded copper
H 4.8 cm; Diam. 10.3 cm
Gift of Victor Gay, 1909; Cl. 17703

Medieval churches were heated only by braziers, unlike certain better-off civilian homes. To ward off the intense cold, high-ranking dignitaries used hand-warmers made of two semispherical cups filled with glowing embers (see the Museum's other complete exhibit).

The cup here is decorated with figures representing the "Liberal Arts". These corresponded with the medieval syllabus: *trivium*, grammar, rhetoric and logic, followed by *quadrivium*, music, astronomy, arithmetic and geometry. The figures here depict *trivium*, together with an ambiguous figure (medecine or arithmetic); the lower half probably illustrated *quadrivium*. This decor was well-suited to the world of clerics who had all undertaken this course of studies.

96

98 Appliqué group: the Flagellation

Limoges, circa 1240-1250
Gilded copper
H 33 cm; W 30 cm
Du Sommerard collection; Cl. 942

While the Limoges workshops of the XIIIth century evolved towards a more traditional production of lesser quality, they were however influenced by the general stylistic development. The Museum's two major appliqué groups, the *Last Supper* and the *Flagellation*, originally part of an ensemble now dispersed (Baltimore, Boston, Minneapolis, Berne), and partially devoted to scenes from the life of Christ, reflect the "stylistic revolution" that occurred in Paris around 1240, in the tormentors' calm, full gestures.

These appliqués also show how the use of enamels on the figures was diminishing, already seen in St. Fausta's great reliquary (**95**), which led to the production of gilded copper objects with enamelled backgrounds destined for large reliquaries, funerary statues or, in this case, altarpieces.

98

99

99 Plaque from an arm-reliquary of St. Victor

France (Champagne?), 1243
Gilded copper
H 18.5 cm; W 10.5 cm
Acq. 1889; Cl. 11981

This finely engraved plaque was the base of an arm-shaped reliquary specially adapted to contain the arm of St. Victor, a VIth-century hermit whose relics were venerated in the Abbey of Montiéramey (Aube). Its exact dating and origin, learnt from the inscription and another text, serve as a valuable landmark in the evolution of goldsmithery in northern France, while reflecting the influence of local taste on the major contemporary trends. One of the inscriptions invokes the saint's protection for a cleric named Philippe, the plaque's purchaser or author, and the main inscription happily combines the execution of the reliquary and the building of a barn.

100

100   **Gemellion**

Limoges, mid-XIIIth century
Gilded copper, champlevé enamel
Diam. 22 cm
Du Sommerard collection; Cl. 954

Gemellion comes from the Latin word
meaning "twin" and thus designated a pair
of basins used for washing hands. One of
them was filled with water that ran into the
second basin through a spout. Like the
aquamaniles (**41**), their use appears ambi-
valent. A decor made up of angels indicates
a religious use, but coats of arms and
scenes of lordly life (hunting, dance, jug-
gling, love scenes, etc.) are more frequent,
thus denoting a secular use, like this basin
adorned with a knight and his lady amid
musicians and arms.

101   **Colonette**

France, mid-XIIIth century
Gilded copper
H 31.7 cm; Diam. (shaft) 1.7 cm
Acq. 1868; Cl. 8677

This colonette most likely came from a
reliquary, as can be seen from its asymme-
trical base and abacus and its installation
marks. It is an example of the technical
perfection of mid-XIIIth-century goldsmiths. The bell of the capital is decorated
with ivy-leaved crockets that were cast
separately from the bell itself; the lower
row of crockets hides the soldering of the
upper row, while its own soldering is hidden by a row of small leaves. The shaft is
stamped with fleurs-de-lys inscribed in
lozenges, a motif reminiscent of the great
royal monuments like the Sainte-Chapelle.
From its size, it may be assumed that this
colonette belonged to one of the splendid
shrines from the Louis IX era that are now
almost all non-existent.

102 Reliquary of St. Lucien, St. Maxien and St. Julien

Paris, shortly after 1261
Gilded silver
H 19.6 cm; L 13.5 cm; W 2.9 cm
Treasury of the Sainte-Chapelle
Gift of Widow Timbal, 1881; Cl. 10746

This precious little reliquary was made to hold the relics of the three saints venerated in Beauvais. According to the *Golden Legend*, Lucien, one of the town's first bishops, together with his two deacons, Maxien and Julien, were decapitated, but miraculously carried their heads, like the Bishop of Paris and t•; companions, Denis, Rustique and Eleuthère. These remains were doubtless given to Louis IX (Saint-Louis) by the Abbot of Saint-Lucien at Beauvais during a special ceremony on 1 May 1261. The reliquary was executed for the Sainte-Chapelle that had just been completed in the heart of the royal palace and is one of the very rare objects preserved from the Treasury. Created in the form of a miniature chapel, it irresistibly recalls the Sainte-Chapelle, but its simplified figures and the high quality of its engraving produce an effect both sobre and monumental.

101

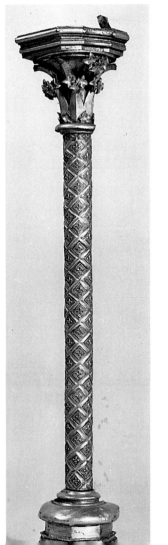

102

103

The Golden Legend tells how St. Helen, the mother of Emperor Constantine, found the Cross of Christ in Jerusalem. It was to become one of the most important relics in Jerusalem, then in Byzantium. The cult of the wood of the True Cross spread throughout Europe during the Crusades, especially after the capture of Constantinople in 1204. To house these fragments reputed to be wood from the True Cross, various types of reliquaries were created, the most frequent of which adopted the double-barred Byzantine cross. The relic was placed in a small compartment; in line with a cult dedicated to the Cross itself, there was generally no figurative decoration, only filigree work and gems.

104 Cylindrical box with courtly decor

Limoges, end of XIIIth century
Gilded copper, champlevé enamel
H 6.1 cm; Diam. 5.1 cm
Victor Gay Coll.
Louvre Deposit; L. OA 6279

The four decorative scenes on this box show it was used for secular purposes, perhaps for keeping ointments or spices. Most of its blue enamel has unfortunately been

104

103 Cross-reliquary of the True Cross

Limoges, c. 1250-c.1275
Filigreed gilded copper on wood, precious stones
Total H 57.3 cm; L 21.4 cm
Soltykoff Coll.
Acq. 1861; Cl. 3294

105

lost, which enables one to get a clearer idea of the champlevé enamel technique - since one can see how the copper plate was cut out and how the resultant spaces were filled in with enamel - and to admire the quality of the engraving. The subject, four couples at different moments of their amorous encounter, recalls that the Limoges workshops, like all medieval artistic centres in the second half of the XIIIth century, increasingly moved towards a production destined for the laity, away from an exclusively religious market.

Guillaume Julien (?)

105 **Six "plique" enamel settings**

Paris, circa 1300
Translucent and opaque enamels on cloisonné gold
approx. H 2.9 cm; L 2.7 cm (two hexagonal plaquettes)
approx. H 3.5 cm; L 3.2 cm (four lozenged plaquettes)
Martin Le Roy Coll.
Gift of J.-J. Marquet de Vasselot, 1930; gift of Mme d'Estallier, 1991; Cl. 21386, 21387, 23411 (a,b,c,d)

The plaquettes with the small rings attached were probably sewn on clothes, like those still found on the imperial stole in the Schatzkammer in Vienna. These settings were known as "plique" enamels, a medieval term applied to the fusing of enamels onto the finest cloisonné framework of gold, a Western revival of the Byzantine technique.

Even if many Parisian goldsmiths used this technique that is frequently referred to in medieval inventories, it is tempting to attribute these works to Guillaume Julien. It was this artist Philip the Fair had commissioned to execute the Sainte-Chapelle's bust-reliquary of Saint Louis, from which a plaquette remains in the Bibliothèque Nationale. The settings here are very similar to this plaquette, as is a work in Oxford whose armorial shield suggests it may have been a wedding present from Philip the Fair to Raoul de Nesle and Isabelle de Hainaut in 1297.

106

106

106

106

106 Pieces from the Colmar Treasure:

Ring

France, XIIIth century
Partially gilded silver
H 2 cm; Diam. 2 cm
Cl. 20665

Jewish wedding ring

Early XIVth century
Gold, enamel, filigree work
H 3.5 cm; Diam. 2.3 cm
Cl. 20658

Trinket

France or Rhineland, first third of
XIVth century
Partially gilded silver
H 2.3 cm; L 2.2 cm
Cl. 20671

Openwork clasp

circa 1325-1350
Gold, precious stones, pearls
H 3.7 cm; L 3.7 cm
Cl. 20672
Treasure found in Colmar in 1863
Acq. 1923

This extraordinary collection of jewellery and coins (**42**), found in the heart of the old Jewish quarter in Colmar, throws light on the medieval Jewish world and its dramatic insecurity. It was most likely buried by a member of the Jewish community of Basel, while fleeing the persecution of the Jews that followed the Great Plague of 1348-1350.

The ring adorned with a leopard and a loving inscription could well be a typical engagement present. But the enamelled ring, given its type and the Hebrew engraving of "good omen", constitutes one of the first known examples of a Jewish wedding ring.

The treasure also contains numerous pieces that were fixed or sewn to clothes: buttons, ornaments or trinkets, like the one of the horseman hunting, and other objects: belts, hooks or clasps were used to hold or fasten a piece of clothing. On the back of the very fine openwork clasp was once a tongue that slipped through a garment into a catch.

Minucchio da Siena

107   **Golden rose**

Avignon, 1330
Gold and coloured glass
(filigreed knot: c. 1250-1275; enamelled
base and shield: post-1330)
H 60 cm
Commissioned by Pope John XXII
Treasury of Basel Cathedral
Gift of Colonel Theubet, 1854; Cl. 2351

Once a year, on the fourth Sunday in Lent (*Laetare*), the Pope would offer a golden rose to a person whose piety he wanted to designate. But, at a time when the Papacy was also a temporal power, this gift could reward more material services. This rose may thus be identified, from the openwork shields added to its base to personalise the artefact (while reusing an older filigreed knot), as being the one offered by Pope John XXII to Rudolph III of Nidau, Count of Neuchâtel. The latter had supported the Pope in his terrible struggle against Emperor Louis of Bavaria. Well-kept papal accounts of the period when the pontiff resided in Avignon name the goldsmith who received the commission; he was one of the Sienese artists who had a decisive influence on art in the papal court, bringing an elegance and naturalism equal to that of Simone Martini in the pictorial field.

107

108

108   **Reliquary-monstrance**

Siena, 1331
Copper, basse-taille enamel on silver,
glass
H 45.5 cm; Diam. 17.7 cm
Eugène Piot Coll.
Acq. 1871; Cl. 9190

The inscription around the base tells us
this work was commissioned by a steward,
but despite its modest nature, it is an inter-

esting reference in the study of Gothic
goldsmithery with its precise 1331 dating.
Its style places it among the production of
Sienese enamellers, who executed their
masterpiece, the reliquary of the Bolsena
corporal for the Cathedral of Orvieto,
during this period. It also offers an
example of the growing religious trend in
the Gothic era of exposing relics or the
Host to view, on the one hand through
transparent reliquaries, which became
monstrances, and on the other, ostensories
that were added to traditional ciboria.

109   **Hanap from the "Treasure of Gaillon"**

France, first half of XIVth century
Partially gilded silver; chased, enamelled
silver medallion
H 5 cm; Diam. 18.5 cm
Acq. 1851; Cl. 1951

This hanap, or drinking cup, belonged to a
group of secular precious metalwork now
dispersed between Paris, London and St.
Petersburg. Made up of hanaps, spoons
and a goblet, it was not, however, a homo-
genous group, as may be seen from the
variety of hallmarks (Paris, Rouen, Mont-
pellier and, on the Museum's goblet,
Amiens) stamped on some of the pieces
and that are among the oldest known town
marks. It was probably collected by a Nor-
man, whose personal mark is found on
certain objects, including this and the
Museum's other hanap, before being
buried at Gaillon, where it was discovered
in obscure circumstances. The absence of
the compulsory silversmith's hallmark
ordered by King John the Good in 1355
(**53**) tends to indicate a dating in the first
half of the XIVth century. The pelican on
the enamelled medallion is a medieval religious theme (it pierces its breast to feed its
children, as Christ gave his blood to save
humanity), but its use as a decorative motif
on a secular object is not surprising.

109

110

110 **Cross-reliquary of the True Cross**

Central France, first half or mid-XIVth century
(base with Brioude hallmark: second half of XVth century)
Gilded silver, gems, pearls, rock crystal
H 21 cm; L 11.4 cm
Wasset Legacy, 1906; Cl. 14793

The simplicity of this cross illustrates the importance of gems and colour to medieval sensibility. The only decoration that enhances the shaft and cross-bar are the stones in cabochon and pearls, recalling the symbolic equivalences clerics established between precious stones, colours, planets and virtues, according to the medieval Lapidaries' treatise. At the time our cross was made, Conrad de Mainbourg used the sapphire as the sign of hope, the emerald as that of purity, the pearl as that of angelic perfection and the diamond as that of strength through suffering.

111

111 Clasp-reliquary

Bohemia (?), mid-XIVth century
Silver, gilded silver, enamels, gems and
pearls
H 18.5 cm; L 18.5 cm
Debruge-Duménil Coll.; Soltykoff Coll.
Acq. 1861; Cl. 3292

This large clasp was used to fasten a high-
ranking ecclesiastical or layman's heavy
coat. It has long been thought a German or
imperial piece of jewellery, because of the
eagle with proudly outstretched wings.
Even if other possible origins exist, the
background of stylised flames and the
crown make its attribution to a Germanic
Emperor of the Bohemian family feasible.

Moreover, the presence of relics in this morse may lead one to think of it as a purely ecclesiastical ornament, but that would be forgetting that princes liked to wear reliquary-jewels as protection, and that the Germanic Holy Roman Emperors were sacred figures (115). King Charles IV of Bohemia, Holy Roman Emperor from 1346-1378, would be one of the best examples of these sovereigns with almost religious power, who was also an enthusiastic relic-lover.

112 Casket

South of France, mid-XIVth century
Gilded copper, champlevé enamel
H 21 cm; L 28.4 cm; W 14.2 cm
Du Sommerard collection; Cl. 979

Abundantly decorated with religious scenes, this small casket also bears four coats of arms of the Canilhac family; its original use is thus ambiguous. Its initial owner could be any one of several members of the Canilhac family from Languedoc who had all, apart from Marquis, the eldest, embraced brilliant religious careers when the Papacy was in Avignon. In style, the work is close to Sienese models imported to Avignon by Simone Martini or his pupil Matteo Giovanetti, the "Pope's painter", while its execution denotes a local, more modest workshop. The ties between the purchaser and the papal court must have been strong, since Marquis' daughter married the Pope's brother in 1345 and Raymond de Canilhac, Archbishop of Toulouse and cardinal in 1350, probably lived at Avignon itself.

113 Cross

Barcelona, 1350-1375
Silver on wood, basse-taille enamel on silver
H 82.5 cm; L 44.5 cm
Henri Leman Coll.
Acq. 1951; Cl. 22585

The hallmark of Barcelona is stamped several times on this fleury cross. Stylistic parallels may be drawn with crosses still in Catalonia or those also bearing the Barcelona stamp. On the contrary, the coats of arms decorating the knot are unique in this series, but still identifiable with Catalonia, more exactly the town of Tarrasca, for which this cross may have been executed. Its slender profile matches the frail elegance of Christ's body and the restrained gestures of the weeping angels.

112

113

Precious arts

114 Virgin and Child and Virgin and the Unicorn

Northern Italy, end of XIVth century
Gilded and engraved glass
H 32.5 cm; W 15 cm
Frédéric Spitzer Coll.
Acq. 1893; Cl.13093

The technique of gilded and engraved glass ("églomisé" according to the term coined by XIXth-century Lyonese collector Carrand) was first used in Roman Antiquity for medallion portraits, then revived in Venice in the second half of the XIIIth century, before spreading all over Italy in the trecento. This picture, similar to late XIVth-century works by Veronese painter Altichiero and Paduan Giusto di Menabuoi, depicts the Virgin and Child crowned and

115

114

seated on a majestic throne, beneath a young girl accompanied by a docile unicorn. This is a representation of the Lady and the Unicorn theme, in which virginity dominates passion and thus becomes queen.

115 Picture-reliquary of St. Genevieve

Paris, circa 1380
Punched and gilded silver, translucent basse-taille enamels on silver
H 8.1 cm; W 6.6 cm
Louis XIV's (?) Coll.; Saint-Cyr House of Royal Education
Acq. 1989; Cl. 23314

The patron saint of Paris is shown in the miracle of the burning candle scene. It is related that while she was provisioning Parisians under siege from Attila, a devil kept blowing out her candle that was relit each time by a guardian angel.

Gothic art's "fin-de-siècle" aesthetics are reflected in this transcription of the story. The little devil with the bellows and the cherub encircling the saint make a delightful small picture. The elegant openwork frame, the quality of the punching in the background decoration, and above all the back of the picture (a peacock amid foliage) underline the preciosity of this miniature reliquary.

On the reverse side, the sliding plaque with the bird engraving protected the compartment containing the relics. Hung on a chain, the picture could be worn to ward off the Devil's attacks that would hopefully be as inoffensive as the one illustrated.

116 Reliquary of the umbilicus of Christ

France (Paris?), 1407
Gilded silver (modern glass capsule)
H 33.4 cm; L 18.9 cm; TH 17.2 cm
Commissioned in 1407 by the testamentary executors of Thibault Des Abbés, a burgher from Châlons-sur-Marne; treasury of Notre-Dame-en-Vaux in Châlons-sur-Marne; Soltykoff Coll.
Acq. 1861; Cl. 3307

116

This statuette of the Virgin and Child is in fact a reliquary of the umbilicus of Christ. Medieval piety greatly esteemed all the remains of Christ and the Virgin, who had however risen to Heaven with their glorious bodies. They thus resorted to the rare corporeal fragments that may have been left on earth: the Virgin's milk, the umbilical cord or foreskin of the Child Jesus, etc. The standing position of the Child on his Mother's right knee is quite rare, but this work is comparable to the finest pieces of Parisian precious metalwork of the International Gothic period, like the Altötting Virgin and Child, given by Queen Isabeau of Bavaria to Charles VI in 1403.

117 Arm-reliquary

France (?), XVth century
Partially gilded silver, enamels, gems
H 48.7 cm; W (base) 13.5 cm
Acq. 1977; Cl. 22887

Relics remained popular from the very early Middle Ages until XVIth-century Reformers and Humanists used this cult as a target for criticism. One of their reproaches was the lack of distinction made between relic and reliquary, often evident in the medieval practise of creating a reliquary in the shape of the relic it was to contain. This arm in the gesture of blessing must have held an arm-bone or hand. The rectangular window edged with an orphrey enabled the viewer to see or check its contents. Only the realistic treatment of the hand offers a dating for this work, otherwise somewhat intemporal in its simplicity.

118 Reliquary-monstrance

Venice, second half of XVth century
Gilded copper, rock crystals, painted
enamels
H 41 cm; W 18 cm
Frédéric Spitzer Coll.; Marchioness
Arconati-Visconti Coll.
Gift 1893; Cl. 13081

The monstrance itself, a rock crystal tube,
is held by three wreathed columns topped
by a cupola; it has a multifoil base decorated with an unusual technique of painted
enamel golden cameo figures on blue background. Similar pieces found in Venice pinpoint its origin. The importance of this

118

117

reliquary-monstrance (see **108**) thus lies in
the fact that it is one of the few remaining
examples of XVth-century Venetian precious metalworks.

Pietro Vannini (?)

119 Processional Cross

Central Italy, second half of XVth century
Gilded silver, translucent enamels, rock
crystals
H 60 cm; W 52 cm
Demidoff Coll.
Acq. 1880; Cl. 9927

The cross, whose indented edges are studded with spherical rock crystals, presents

119

an agonising Christ surrounded by the Virgin, St. Peter, St. John and Mary-Magdalen at his feet, in typical Italian fashion. These figures stand out in high relief, like those, on the back, of God the Father and the four Evangelists' symbols, in contrast with the translucent enamels of the lozenge-shaped medallions. The work should be attributed to Pietro Vannini, a goldsmith active at Ascoli Piceno between 1452 and 1495.

120 **Reliquary**

Germany, 1469
Gilded copper
H 9 cm; W 7.5 cm
Piet-Lataudrie Coll.
Piet-Lataudrie Legacy, 1915; Cl. 19968

This historiated, box-shaped reliquary may have been made in imitation of a manuscript binding. The scenes depicted are inspired from contemporary engravings, which illustrates the close ties that existed between goldsmiths and engravers. The Crucifixion scene is a copy of an engraving attributed to Israël van Meckenem; on the other side, dated 1469, the Christ in the Garden of Olives scene is taken from a composition by the Master of playing cards, dated around 1450.

Hans Greiff

121 Statue-reliquary of St. Anne the Trinitarian

Ingolstadt, 1472
Partially gilded painted silver
H 48.6 cm; L 21 cm
Commissioned by Anna Hofmann, wife of Ingolstadt tax-receiver; Soltykoff Coll.; Debruge-Duménil Coll.
Acq. 1861; Cl. 3308

At the end of the Middle Ages, and especially in Germany, the cult of St. Anne, mother of the Virgin, was widespread. Artists frequently represented the theme of St. Anne the Trinitarian (*Anna selbdritt*), with the ancestor holding both the Virgin Mary and the Child Jesus on her knees. Here, the latter hold the reliquary itself and Jesus is depicted as having the same

121

120

age as his mother, an unlikely but frequent detail.

Such an iconography is further explained by St. Anne being the purchaser's patron saint. A long inscription on the back informs us of the latter's name, wife of the local tax-receiver, the work's delivery date, Michaelmas Day, 1472, the goldsmith's name and even the amount paid. Thanks to this piece, other works have been attributed to Hans Greiff, a Bavarian goldsmith in practise up to 1516.

122 Crucifixion

Burgundy (?), second half of XVth century
Gilded painted copper; back: paint on
wood
H 66 cm; L 51 cm
Albert de Roucy Coll.
Acq. 1858; Cl. 2800

On the back of the panel may be found the
emblem, a flaming torch emerging from a
wooden flap (*huchette*), and motto ("Nul ne
s'y frotte" - "Nobody interferes") of
Anthony (1421-1504), the illegitimate son
of the Duke of Burgundy, Philip the Good.
This motto suited he who was nicknamed
the "Great Bastard of Burgundy" and
famed for his bravery, especially at the
Battle of Nancy, in 1477, during which he
lost his half-brother, Charles the Bold.
The applied copper figures of the Crucifixion on the front belong to the Duchy of
Burgundy's artistic production and are
comparable with the works of the last great
ducal "imager", Antoine Le Moiturier.

123 Crossbow insignia

Cleves, circa 1500
Gilded silver
H 12 cm (main part); W 6 cm
Louis Fould Coll.; Cloquet Coll.
Cloquet Donation, 1860; Cl. 3027

In urban society of the Late Middle Ages,
guilds, or companies, of archers and crossbowmen often played an important role, by
preparing citizens to help in their town's
defence, and also at social events. These
guild badges, worn by the head of the guild
or given as a prize at annual games meetings, are a reminder of their members'
activities. This miniature shield-shaped
badge hanging from a crown, has a cross-
bow decoration together with its target of a
bird on a branch. The figures of the Virgin
and Child, next to St. Hermes, patron saint
of Warbeyen, near Cleves, pinpoints its
small Rhineland town of origin.

122

123

hypothesis suggests its purchaser may have been a cleric in the suite of Louis XII, as both figures are represented at the foot of the Cross. This ecclesiastic might have commissioned the work to commemorate the treaty signed in Lyons, on 1st April 1503, by Louis XII and his enemy, the son-in-law of the King of Aragon. In this treaty, the King of France abandoned his claims to the crown of Naples, inherited by King René of Anjou (whose arms are behind the King), as symbolised by the small crown on the ground.

124

Nardon Pénicaud

124 **The Crucifixion**

Limoges, 1503 (?)
Copper, painted enamels
H 31 cm; L 23.3 cm
Labadie Legacy, 1853; Cl. 2232

This enamelled plaque is a reference point in several ways. In the second half of the XVth century, the workshops of the Limoges enamellers that, since 1350, had been gradually dying out, underwent a revival with the use of the technique of enamel painted on copper. Instead of the three-dimensional artefacts of the XIIIth century, they were to supply secular or devotional "pictures" until the beginning of the XVIIth century. The presence of a rare signature and date make this *Crucifixion* a unique example. Enameller Nardon Pénicaud was known from 1493 to his death, and his harmonious production was identified due to this work. An ingenious

125 **Belt**

Germany, circa 1520
Silk, gilded silver, gems
L 145 cm; W 2.2 cm
Debruge-Duménil Coll.
Acq. 1850; Cl. 1835

This belt is typical of Late German Gothic ornamental art, at the time of Dürer. It is decorated with rosettes and other flowers represented in the naturalist mode, while the buckle is lyre-shaped. A drawing by Hans Holbein the Younger, dated 1523-1526, which depicts an elegant Basel noblewoman wearing an almost identical belt, establishes a similar dating and a probable Upper-Rhineland origin.

125 (detail)

Wood, ivory, stone

Sculptors in the Middle Ages used a large variety of materials. Works were not only cut in stone, but also in other minerals like marble, alabaster, or hard stones such as crystal. A great number of mediums from the plant kingdom were also used: oak, poplar, lime, walnut and some fruit-tree woods. Lastly, materials from the animal kingdom were not excluded: ivory, from both elephant and walrus, and bone. The use of a specific medium varied from region to region and also depended on its availability. The remarkable rise in carved ivories in the XIIIth century was thus due to a more plentiful supply.

Working conditions for sculptors in the Late Middle Ages are better known than those of earlier periods. The increase in production - consider the vast construction sites of Gothic cathedrals and the evolution of devotional sculpture - led to radical changes in the profession, from the XIIIth century onwards. Corporations with strictly defined rules laid down rigid frameworks. According to the *Book of Crafts* by Etienne Boileau, Parisian merchants' provost, at the end of the XIIIth century, the craft of "imager-cutters" belonged among the luxury trades, unlike that of carpenters, which included makers of wooden hutches (**189**). Members of the former corporation were exempt from certain taxes and dues. It was made up of cutters, or sculptors, of statues in wood, stone, bone, horn and ivory, who could thus work at will in several mediums. Creations by contemporary Italian Giovanni Pisano

Sculpture

bear witness to this, as sculptures of his in wood, stone, marble and ivory have been preserved. The Nottingham sculptures in alabaster (**184**), or those of the Florentine Embriachi, specialised in bone and wooden caskets and altarpieces (**175**), were produced in highly organised workshops.

While evidence of moulding and modelling may exist (**187**), cutting remains the most frequently used technique. Contrary to an accepted opinion, stone was not hewn directly, the artist's work being preceded by a series of preparatory stages: finished design, gradual rough hewing following working drawings in most cases. In the great sculpted cycles, certain standards had to be observed from one statue to another. The same tools were always used in cutting: chisels, gouges, rasps, trepans and gradines of various sizes depending on the volume or nature of the piece to be executed. Works were generally cut from a single block, except crucifixes (**147-148**), the limbs of which could be added later.

Painting was the final stage in the execution of a sculpture and was done by the sculptor himself or another artist. As in the preparation of a painted panel, an undercoat was put on the statue before the final application of paint or gilding. This last stage was essential, and the loss of colour gives one a false impression of the sculpture of the period, which shows the importance of well-preserved works (**174**).

Dany Sandron

126

127   Pillar of Saint-Landry

Paris, second half of IInd century
Stone
Total reconstructed height: over 170 cm
Paris, Ile da la Cité
Du Sommerard collection;
reinv. in 1912; Cl. 18606-18608

Three carved fragments found in 1829, on
the site of the church of Saint-Landry on
the Ile de la Cité, seem to have been part of
a votive pillar; on the best-preserved element are the gods Mars and Vulcan and a
female deity, perhaps Vesta. Only the
lower half of three figures, identified as
Jupiter (in the middle) Mercury and
Minerva, are found on the second, very
framentary element. The last element,
whose place in the monument is sometimes

126   Pillar of the Nautes

Paris, 14-37 A.D.
Stone
Total reconstructed height: over 250 cm
Paris, Ile de la Cité
Ecole des Beaux-Arts Deposit, 1844;
reinv. in 1912; Cl. 18602-18605

These four, separately-displayed, sculpted
blocks are the remains of a monument that,
according to the dedication, was offered to
Jupiter by the corporation of the Seine
Boatmen, under the reign of Tiberius. By
comparing earlier Greek examples and
later vestiges in Gaul and Germania, we
may reconstruct a pillar formed by piling
up these elements, doubtless topped by a
statue of Jupiter. Gallic divinities (Esus,
Cernunnos, Smertrios..) mingle indiscrimi-
nately with Roman gods (Jupiter, Vulcan,
Castor, Pollux..), most frequently identified
by inscriptions, together with six figures
traditionally associated with the town
magistrates or boatmen who controlled
navigation on the Seine. The syncretism of
the carvings that blends local and Roman
divinities testifies to the success of the
cultural amalgamation initiated by Caesar.

127

questioned, bears an unidentified figure, a rosette and the same decorative motif of overlapping leaves as found on the back of the other two fragments, which tends to prove it was an addorsed pillar. The presence of Roman gods does not eliminate the continued underlying existence of Gallic mythology whose divinities would be represented by their Roman homologues. Thus, more than a century after the Pillar of the Nautes (**126**), elements of the Gallic religion survived through the portrayal of classical types. The lithe, slender-bodied figures, stamped in some cases with a real sense of pathos, are fine examples of the Neo-Atticism that spread throughout the Empire from Hadrian's time onwards.

128　Statue of Julian the Apostate

> 361-400 A.D.
> Greek marble (from Naxos?)
> H 180 cm
> Brought from Italy to Paris around 1787;
> Dumont Coll.
> Acq. 1859; Cl. 18830

This figure combines features borrowed from representations of Greek philosophers (toga, pallium, volumen) and from portraits of pagan priests (diadem). He was identified as Emperor Julian the Apostate (361-364) from his minted effigy. The existence of similar statues (Louvre; a head in Thasos) tally well with an imperial portrait. Julian openly proclaimed his pagan beliefs, after being declared Emperor in 361. He then let his beard grow and the statue is thus posterior to this date. It may have been sculpted after his death, which would explain the pupilless eyes, a treatment reserved for funerary or heroic works. In this case, it would have been commissioned by one of the still-flourishing pagan circles of the late IVth century (**129**).

128

129 Panel from the diptych of the Nicomachi and the Symmachi

Rome (?), circa 400
Ivory
H 29 cm; W 12 cm
Abbey church of Montier-en-Der (diocese of Langres)
Acq. 1882; Cl. 17048

This scene shows a priestess of Ceres practising a pagan rite in honour of Cybele. The panel was originally part of a diptych whose other half (in the Victoria and Albert Museum in London) depicts a sacrifice to Jupiter by a priestess of Bacchus. The names, Nicomachi and Symmachi, engraved on the two leaves are those of two illustrious Roman senatorial families. The diptych may have been executed to commemorate a marriage between two members of these families, unless it was to celebrate certain pagan cults to which the traditional aristocracy remained devoted, even after 382 when the State stopped their subsidies. Iconographically, this pagan "manifesto" is clearly of classical inspiration.

By an irony of fate, these two panels owe their survival to having been mounted on a reliquary to St. Bercharius, founder of the Abbey of Montier-en-Der.

130 Panel from the diptych of the Consul Areobindus

Constantinople, 506
Ivory
H 39 cm; W 13 cm
Dijon, possibly end of XVIIth century; Baudot Coll.
Acq. 1894; Cl. 13135

From the end of the IVth century onwards, consuls used to celebrate their accession to office by sending out ivory diptychs, whose interior surface could be used as a writing tablet. The outside was decorated with the effigy of the consul, either isolated or in an appropriate setting; inscriptions specified the name and titles. The Musée de Cluny's panel, identified through comparison with other panels (in Zurich, Besançon, Lucca), was a leaf from a diptych offered by Consul Areobindus, in 506.

The representation of a consul presiding over the opening of the celebratory games, known as the "tribune of an amphitheatre" type, was quite frequent. Certain details however may be strictly relevant to Areobindus' career; the two victories on either end of the seat could thus refer to his prowess as a warrior.

The weakness of the relief and stereotype figures, with round faces and fixed expressions, are typical of early VIth-century consular diptychs from Constantinople.

129

131 Appliqué group: Ariadne, maenad, satyr and cupids

Constantinople, first half of VIth century
Ivory
H 40 cm; W 14 cm
Du Sommerard collection; Cl. 455

This large figure of Ariadne, accompanied by a maenad, a satyr and two crown-bearing cupids, and holding Bacchus' wand, or thyrsus, and a cup, was carved in bold relief out of half an elephant's tusk. It was possibly intended to decorate a piece of furniture, a seat - like the famous throne of Bishop Maximianus of Ravenna - or a bed, with a matching statue of Bacchus.
The quality of the finely-polished ivory-work makes this one of the masterpieces of early VIth-century Constantinopolitan art.

130

131

It has the same powerful style as the Barberini ivory in the Louvre and the finest consular or imperial diptychs of the era. The figures adopt supple or even sensual poses, as here, while the perfectly oval, sultry-looking faces convey the period's lingering aristocratic taste for the luxury and opulence of subjects taken from pagan mythology.

132

132 Lion heads

Roman Empire, 1st half of IVth-2nd half
of VIth centuries(?)
Quartz
H 12 cm; W 9 cm; D 10 cm
Du Sommerard collection; Cl. 615-616

These two lion heads are considered to
have been ornaments of a consular or
imperial throne, by analogy with the representations of thrones in Late Antiquity in
mosaics (Santa Maria Maggiore in Rome),
sculptures, sarcophagi, ivories and above
all coins, especially those of the Emperors
Arcadius, Honorius and Attalus, between
the IVth and VIth centuries. This decorative element may have been chosen for its
biblical ancestry, the lion being associated
with Solomon's throne, but more vaguely
oriental references cannot be eliminated.
On the strength of allegations made by
their purchaser Alexandre Du Sommerard,
who had, without proof, pinpointed their
discovery to a Rhineland tomb, these
pieces were long attributed to Trèves,
where a glyptics workshop is known to
have existed in the Late Byzantine Empire.
However, the possibility of a different provenance, either Eastern or Western, cannot
be excluded. The lack of comparable pieces
also prevents a precise dating.

133 Capital

South-west Gaul (?), Vth- VIIth centuries
(?)
Pyrenean marble
H 43 cm; W 51 cm
Saint-Denis, Basilica or Church of
St. Peter
Storeroom of Saint-Denis, assigned in
1890; Cl. 12114 A

The decor is freely inspired from the classical Corinthian capital with three rows of
leaves, volutes and caulicoli under the
rosettes marking the centre of each side of
the bell. Parallels may be drawn between
the characteristic treatment here of soft
leaves with prominent central vein and

133

134

other examples from south-west Gaul (Tor-rebren, in the Gers; Poitiers; baptistry of Saint-Jean and Saint-Hilaire-le-Grand...), together with sarcophagi from Aquitaine, where these capitals originated, before being distributed throughout Gaul.

According to XIXth-century archeologists and architects, this was one of the capitals found among the stonework in the bell-towers of the Basilica of Saint-Denis. But these sculptures may also come from the chevet of the neighbouring church of St. Peter, since it is known to have been ador-ned on the outside by marble capitals and columns.

134 **Diptych**

England, second half of VIIIth century (?)
(obverse); Northern Italy (?), circa 900
(reverse)
Ivory
H 34.3 cm; W 10.7 cm (each plaque)
Treasury of the Cathedral of Beauvais (?)
Du Sommerard collection; Cl. 391

This diptych is distinguished by its sculpted decor on each side, the oldest of which depicts Christological scenes (the Annunciation, Crucifixion, Abraham's Sacrifice on one plaque; Baptism of Christ and Ascension, on another). The work is considered to be of VIIIth-century Anglo-Saxon origin, after comparisons with minia-tures executed between 500 and 1000 and two ivories illustrating the Baptism of Christ and the Ascension (Victoria and Albert Museum, London), as well as a Crucifixion scene (Bayerisches Nationalmuseum, Munich).

Ivory being a rare and costly material, these sculptures were later planed down, to be reused as a decorative manuscript binding, at which point carvings of exuberant leafy scrolls filled with real or fabulous figures and creatures - lions, centaurs, Tritons, satyrs - were executed on the back. This return to themes from classical mythology is typical of the IXth-century Carolingian Renaissance. A Christian connotation evoking the Creation may also exist, as in the case of the ivories from the flabellum of Tournus (Florence, Bargello) or the Chair of St. Peter's in Rome.

135 Plaque from a binding: the Crowning of Otto II and Theophano

Germanic Empire, 982-983
Ivory
H 18 cm; W 10 cm
Du Sommerard collection; Cl. 392

135

Under a dais supported by columns, Christ is seen crowning Otto II and Theophano. Latin inscriptions on the background of the plaque identify this imperial couple. At the Emperor's feet a figure lies prostrate before Christ; his invocation is engraved in Greek characters and reveals the donator's name, John, who is generally thought to be the Bishop of Plaisance, John Philagathos. A frequent visitor to the Ottonian court from 980 onwards, he helped establish cordial relations between the Germanic and Byzantine Empires.

The subject and composition of the plaque are typically Byzantine, reproducing the composition an ivory of Christ crowning Emperor Romanus II and Eudocia found in the Bibliothèque Nationale in Paris. The style is so influenced by Byzantine art that it is assumed to be the work of an artist from Byzantium established in the West. Few works offer such a clear illustration of

the close ties that existed, at the end of the Xth century, between the West and Byzantium, whose fascinating influence remained unbroken in the West.

136 Plaque from a binding: Crucifixion, Holy Women at the Tomb, Ascension and Parousia

Rhineland (Cologne?), end of Xth-early XIth centuries
Ivory
H 17 cm; W 11 cm
Frédéric Spitzer Coll.
Acq. 1893; Cl. 13064

The main scene is featured on the Cross that cuts the plaque into four and covers a complex eschatological programme typical of Carolingian ivories: first, the Crucifixion with St. John and the Virgin raising their eyes to Christ, clad in a long tunic (*colobium*); then, the Holy Women at the tomb on Easter morning, greeted by an angel; in the top right-hand corner, the hand of God stretches towards his Son, accompanied by four angels and witnessed by the Apostles and the Virgin; finally, the cycle closes with Christ of the Parousia, in a mandorla encircled by the symbols of the four Evangelists. The style is close to a plaque showing Christ between St. Gereon and St. Victor (Schnütgen Museum, Cologne), whose iconography and similarity to illuminated works from Cologne provides an origin and a dating of around 1000. Together with ivories from Liège, these works bear witness to the vitality of the Rhineland-Meuse workshops in the Ottonian period, in which the tradition of imperial Carolingian art lived on.

137   Plaque from a binding: St. Paul

Echternach (?), 1025-1050
Ivory
H 21 cm; W 10 cm; TH 2 cm
Acq. 1844; Cl. 1505

St. Paul, with his characteristic baldness and long beard, is carved from a plaque of unusual thickness (2cm), the holes in which prove it was part of a binding. On the scroll he is holding, a quotation from his first Epistle to the Corinthians leaves us in no doubt as to his identity: "But by the grace of God, I am what I am".

This highly statuesque, fierce figure of St. Paul belongs to a group of four, all sharing the same style and attributed to the same artist: a diptych (Moses receiving the Tables of the Law, the Doubts of St. Thomas) and a Christ in Majesty, both in Berlin, and a Crucifixion mounted on the front of a binding of a Codex Aureus from Echternach (Germanisches nationalmuseum, Nuremberg). The established origin of the manuscript kept in Nuremberg, in addition

136

137

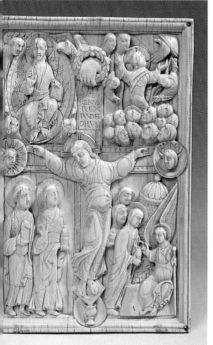

to the stylistic ties between these ivories and the Echternach manuscripts, pinpoints the activity of this sculptor to the sumptuous abbey in the Trèves region around 1025-1050.

138 Capital from Saint-Germain-des-Prés

Paris, mid-XIth century
Stone
H 72 cm
Paris, nave of the abbey church of Saint-Germain-des-Prés
Gift of the City of Paris; reinv. in 1912;
Cl.18612

The Museum's twelve capitals from the nave of Saint-Germain-des-Prés, deposited during the major XIXth-century restoration project, represent one of the key works of early Romanesque sculpture in the Ile-de-France that was closely linked to architectural development. The appearance of supports made up of several columns set in a massive square went hand in hand with the widespread use of figurative capitals, also adorned with ancient plant motifs.
On the capital featuring Christ in a mandorla, flanked by angels, two styles are evident: one, typically Romanesque, raises the highly-stylised figure on the right of the

bell in flattened planes; the other treats Christ and the angel on the left much more freely, unconcerned about the framework offered by the bell, playfully twisting the angel's body round the angle column. Parallels may be found in certain works of Ottonian goldsmithery.

139 Oliphant

South Italy, end of XIth-early XIIth centuries
Ivory
H 64 cm
Treasury of the Abbey of Saint-Arnoul of Metz;
Frédéric Spitzer Coll.
Acq. 1893; Cl. 13065

Derived from the word elephant, oliphants were carved out of the end of the tusk. In the Middle Ages they were used as musical instruments, drinking horns or relic-holders, hence their relatively frequent presence in church treasuries. The Museum's oliphant was carved towards the end of the XIth century in southern Italy, a region then renowned for its ivory trade and its specialisation in caskets, chess pieces and oliphants. Curiously, only the ends of the tusk were sculpted at first with a series of decorative bands inspired by Fatimid art.

138

Later, the previously bare central zone was carved with an Ascension scene and the Evangelists' symbols, an iconography strongly influenced by Byzantine art, while the formal bas-relief treatment with very schematised figures is reminiscent of Lombard art.

140 Capital

Paris, circa 1100
Stone
L 114 cm; H 46 cm
Paris, nave of the Abbey of Sainte-Geneviève
Ecole des Beaux-Arts Deposit

The Romanesque Abbey of Sainte-Geneviève, one of Paris' most prestigious institutions and burial place of the capital's patron saint, was demolished except for its belltower during the XIXth century. Four large capitals originally crowned huge columns over five metres high at the entrance to the nave and were decorated with signs of the zodiac, scenes from Genesis and plant motifs. Their remarkably free treatment, visible in the foliage and such figures as the nude representing Aquarius, evokes an almost profane, yet cultured atmosphere, which is hardly surprising given the intellectuel wealth of such establishments on Mount Sainte-Geneviève.

139

140

141 Head of a crozier

England, circa 1120-1130
Walrus ivory
H 15 cm
Frédéric Spitzer Coll.
Acq. 1893; Cl. 13066

Walrus ivory was a material currently
employed in northern European countries,
including England, not necessarily due to a
lack of elephant ivory. It was used to make
chess and other games' pieces, as well as
for more prestigious religious objects like
this crozier that is lavishly adorned with
foliated scrolls, animals and monsters and
incrusted with pearls. On each side, an
eagle and a lion - perhaps Evangelists'
symbols - are found in the centre of the
volute treading on a dragon's head, as if to
portray the victory of the divine word over
evil, a theme often featured on bishops and
abbots' emblems of power.

The form and openwork decoration on the
head of the crozier are technically close to
those of St. John of Beverley's crook (British
Museum, London), while the decor is
also characteristic of the kind used in Can-

142

141

terbury manuscripts around 1120-1130,
and in an ivory tau (Victoria and Albert
Museum, London), similar to Winchester
illumination in the first half of the century.

142 Head of a queen

Saint-Denis, pre-1140
Stone
H 32 cm; W 20 cm
Façade of the Abbey of Saint-Denis
Acq. 1986; Cl. 23250

The triumphal composition of the three
portals on the façade of Saint-Denis, consecrated
in 1140 under Suger's abbacy, was
seriously mutilated in the XVIIIth and
XIXth centuries. One of the outstanding
features of this work, the huge column-statues
lined up along the splays, was only
known through the engravings of Montfaucon's
Les Monuments de la monarchie

française, published in 1729, and in three badly damaged heads in the United States (Baltimore and Cambridge). ·

The recent discovery of this head of a queen, since joined by a head of Moses and a second prophet's head, gives one a clearer idea of the exceptional nature of the former sculpted Gothic portal. The face's fierce, brutally frank expression and precise, strong features reminiscent of works in metal, convey a highly personal, unprecedented approach that had no immediate sequel.

These larger-than-life-sized statues represent figures from the Old Testament and not the kings and queens of France as once thought; this head is very likely that of the Queen of Sheba.

143 **St. Peter, fragment**

Paris, circa 1150
Stone
H 122 cm; W 40 cm; TH 31 cm
Notre-Dame de Paris, west façade,
St. Anne portal
Discovered in 1839, attributed in 1843;
Cl. 18658

Thanks to Montfaucon's engravings (**142**), this fragment has been identified as the lower part of a statue of St. Peter from the St.Anne portal of Notre-Dame. Kings and queens of the Old Testament together with St.Peter and St. Paul lined the embrasures of this portal, while the trumeau featured St. Marcel. Around 1210, the portal was reset into the present façade then under construction. Since the sculptures date from around 1150, before erection of the Gothic Cathedral of Notre-Dame had even begun, this makes the St. Anne portal, together with the royal portal of Chartres, one of the earliest examples of Gothic sculpture.

The fragment of St. Peter attests to the extraordinary quality of this group: the coat falls apart at the bottom to reveal the robe's fine pleats descending to the feet; the strong pure lines of the drapery fall vertically over the right leg, while the meandering folds over the left leg outline curious smooth areas.

143

144 Statue of a prophet

Paris region, circa 1170
Stone
H 103 cm
Inv. in 1912; Cl. 18659

With phylactery in hand and round hat on
his head, this figure is unmistakably a prophet. The facial expression, the high prominent cheekbones, the fixed stare and the
tightness of the drapery around the stocky
body all underline the figure's vehemence
and the powerful message to be delivered.
The detached column behind the statue
proves that it was intended to adorn a
portal or cloister, doubtless in or near
Paris, since it is carved from the best-qua-
lity Lutetian limestone.

Stylistically close to statues from the portal
of Senlis Cathedral, to figures on the archi-
volts in Mantes, and also to sculpture from
the Valois door in the north transept of
Saint-Denis, this figure of a prophet is a
fine example of Ile-de-France sculpture's
search for greater expressivity in the years
around 1170.

144

145 Draughts piece: battle between men and dragons

Northern Europe (England or
Scandinavia)
XIIth century
Walrus ivory
Diam. 5.5 cm
Sachs Donation, 1951; Cl. 22591

During the Romanesque period, draughts
and backgammon pieces were often decorated with animal motifs or more complex
scenes. This piece has a pearl border
around the central scene of a fight between
two men and two dragons. It depicts one of
the labours of Hercules in which the Greek
hero and his companion Iolaus affront the
Lernaean hydra. Some versions of the story
refer to the presence of a second monster.
It is very similar to a piece in Florence and

is carved from walrus ivory, a common
substitute for elephant ivory in northern
Europe at this time.

146 Capital

Catalonia, end of XIIth century
Stone
H 27 cm; W 27 cm
Acq. 1881; reinv. 1912; Cl. 19002

Cloisters were often richly decorated in the
XIIth century. The Catalonian examples in
the Cathedral of Gerona, St. Peter's of
Rodez and Sant Cugat del Vallès are some
of the period's finest creations. The six
capitals in the Museum are from the same
workshops, whose skill in depicting scenes
from the life of Christ was combined with a
rare sense of narrative that is visible in the
singular episode of the holy women buying
aromatic oils, before going to the sepulchre
to embalm the body of Christ on Easter
morning. XIIIth-century sensibility is
conveyed through the scene's pervasive
simplicity.

146

145

147

147 Christ on the Cross

Auvergne, XIIth century
Polychrome wood (poplar)
H 158 cm
Dation, 1991; CL.23409

This great figure of Christ is one of the rare examples of large Romanesque devotional sculptures of French origin. Like the famous Auvergne Virgins in Majesty that copied the now non-existent Virgin of Clermont, these statues of Christ on the Cross may have reproduced an especially venerated figure of Christ.

This sculpture is parallel to a group of schematically similar Romanesque Christs preserved in Auvergne, with the same frontal position of the body, outstretched legs, and symmetrical arrangement of the perizonium (loincloth), tied in the middle of the abdomen. Furthermore, this Christ was found in the Auvergne region, at the end of the XIXth century, in the former commandery of the Knights of St. John of Jerusalem at Le Puy (Haute-Loire), part of whose church dated back to the XIIth century. The expressive qualities of the Le Puy Christ belong to the Late Romanesque period, at the dawn of a new sensibility. He is shown dead, with eyes closed and his head on his right shoulder: no longer Christ triumphant and majestic, but Christ in agony, a theme that would prove prolific in Gothic sculpture.

148 **Christ on the Cross**

France, circa 1200
Polychrome wood (pear-tree)
H 178 cm
Mallay Donation, 1852; Cl. 2169

Few of the great Christs on the Cross that hung over church altars or under arched ceilings have survived, but this Christ remains one of the finest examples of early Gothic large devotional sculpture.

The refinement of the knotted perizonium, once enhanced by colour, the subtle model-ling of the face and body, the fixed melan-cholic gaze and the carefully arranged strands of the beard make this a figure of great authority tempered however by the softness of the features. The artist was indiscutably familiar with large-scale sculpture from Burgundy, or northern France; one should thus remain cautious in attributing this work to a distinct area like Auvergne, merely because it is here that the majority of these statues have escaped the throws of time.

148

149

around 1200 was marked by a return to classicized tendencies springing from a XIIth-century revival of classical culture and frequent contact with Byzantium. Paris was affected by this movement, which spread to most of western Europe, influencing all art forms from painting and sculpture to precious metalwork.

150

149 **Torso of an apostle**

Paris, circa 1210
H 96 cm
Notre-dame de Paris, west façade, central portal
Discovered in 1839; attributed in 1887;
Cl. 18657

Most of the original tympanum and voussoirs of the central portal on the façade of Notre-Dame de Paris are still standing, but the statues of the twelve apostles that filled their splays and of Christ, on the trumeau, were lost during the Revolution and replaced in the XIXth century. A few fragments, including this torso of an apostle, have however survived.

The deeply carved, sinuous folds of the coat's drapery covering the left shoulder and girdling the waist recalls the statuary of classical antiquity. The whole period

150 **Head of a prelate**

Paris, 1210-1220
Stone
H 38 cm
Notre-Dame de Paris, west façade, portal of the Coronation of the Virgin
Discovered in 1839; inv. in 1906;
Cl. 16602

The left portal on the façade of Notre-Dame de Paris is devoted to the Virgin. Worship of Mary had grown so important since the second half of the XIIth century that most great churches started consecrating a portal to the Mother of God. In Paris, she was also the patron saint of the cathedral, which explains why the Virgin and Child appear on the trumeau, accompanied by the saints of the diocese, including St. Denis, St. Geneviève and a bishop, perhaps St. Germain, whose head is preserved here and identified from the vestiges of his mitre and lappets.

New density of volume and sureness of line convey the changing trend around 1220 towards a harder, more simplified style than the classicized art of the beginning of the century. This prelate's head, with the tympanum of the portal of the Virgin, the Saint-Germain-l'Auxerrois portals and a statue of St. Geneviève from the eponymous Parisian abbey (Louvre) testify to Paris' decisive role in the definition of this style reflected in the façade of Amiens Cathedral.

151

151 Head of a king

Paris, 1220-1230
H 65 cm; W 40 cm; D 40 cm
Notre-Dame de Paris, west façade,
Gallery of the Kings
Gift of the Banque Française du
Commerce Extérieur, 1980; Cl. 22997

Above the portals on the façade of Notre-Dame stretched the Gallery of the Kings, made up of twenty-eight colossal statues, all of which were remade in the XIXth century. The originals had been removed and placed in front of the cathedral, in 1793, when all royal insignia were suppressed.

One of the most spectacular discoveries made in the rue de la Chaussée d'Antin, in 1977, was perhaps that of twenty-one kings' heads believed to have been lost forever. Despite their mutilated condition that added even greater emotional impact, these giant figures, with facial features enhanced by surprisingly well-preserved polychromy, can be stylistically reset in the line of portals on the façade.

From the XIIIth century onwards, these statues were traditionally seen as effigies of the Kings of France, but they may originally have been meant to depict the Kings of Judah, ancestors of the Virgin, who, flanked by two angels, topped the composition, in front of the great rose. Other Galleries of Kings in the Cathedrals of Chartres, Amiens and Rheims attest to the success of royal iconography in the XIIIth century.

152 Virgin and Child

Meuse region (?), circa 1220-1230
Ivory
H 30 cm
Du Sommerard collection; Cl. 398

After long years of shortage, XIIIth-century Christian Europe once more enjoyed an abundant supply of prestigious elephant ivory, prized for its whiteness and purity. Medieval symbolism knew no better medium for depicting seated, sovereign Virgins than ivory, the material used for

152

Tuscany, circa 1220-1230
Polychrome wood
H 170 cm
Acq. 1854; Cl. 2369

A statue of the Virgin and this statue of St. John were both part of a Deposition from the Cross group that may also have included statues of Joseph of Arimathaea and Nicodemus; the figure of Christ is still

153

Solomon's throne. Thus it may not be fortuitous if Gothic ivorywork began with the great statues of seated Virgins, the finest examples of which are in the Musée de Cluny, the Hermitage (St. Petersburg), and the Petit Palais (Paris). Stylistic parallels can be drawn with wooden sculptures from the Meuse region, which were in turn influenced by artistic centres of northern and north-eastern France, at a time of intensive research and formal exchange, before Parisian workshops took the lead.

found today in the Cathedral of Prato. The ensemble belongs to the large groups sculpted during the first half of the XIIIth century in Umbria and Tuscany (Tivoli, Volterra), which depicted Christ's Descent from the Cross, at that time a more popular theme than the Crucifixion, and which stressed Christ's humanity by henceforth showing him dead.

These humanised figures were part of the great move, in the early XIIIth century, towards artforms more responsive to the beauty of this world. Simplicity of volume is combined with sumptuous colours that were restored in the XIVth century and remain remarkably well-preserved, giving one a vivid idea of the effect they must once have had on the faithful.

154 **Apostle from the Sainte-Chapelle**

Paris, 1241-1248
Stone
H 165 cm
Paris, Sainte-Chapelle
Musée des Monuments Français; calvary
of Mount Valerian;
Attributed in 1850; reinv. in 1912;
Cl. 18665

Against the pillars in the high chapel, twelve statues of apostles, each bearing his emblem and a sacred cross, formed a procession behind Christ, present in the distinguished relics of the crown of thorns, for which St. Louis had ordered the Sainte-Chapelle to be built. All the statues were removed under the Revolution; the six that were not put back during the XIXth-century restoration works are now in the Musée de Cluny.

The melancholic expression of one of these six statues highlights the exceptional quality of the works. Together with statues from the northern arm of the transept in Notre-Dame de Paris and from the jube in Bourges Cathedral, they indisputably mark the zenith of mid-XIIIth-century Parisian classicism. The harmony of the balanced gestures, sober drapery and serene ex-

154

pressions evokes that rare moment of an artform tranquilly relishing its perfection. In the Sainte-Chapelle itself, one may find examples of a more restless style in other figures of apostles that foreshadow certain mannerist trends of the second half of the XIIIth century.

155

155 Fragment from a diptych

Paris, circa 1250
H 19 cm; W 8 cm
Du Sommerard collection; Cl. 417

Although the bottom corners of this ivory plaque are missing, the existing scenes of the Road to Calvary and Leviathan, topped by a series of openwork gables, have been matched with another plaque (in Walters Art gallery, Baltimore) to reconstitute a diptych illustrating Christ's Passion. This kind of object revived an ancient tradition in ivorywork (**130**) that had never really died out, set in a totally new context. Stylistically close to monumental sculpture, these diptychs were in fact intended for the devotions of the laity and depicted scenes from the life of Christ or eschatological visions of the Last Judgement and the Coronation of the Virgin.

This leaf belongs to the so-called "Soissons" group that includes a complete diptych thought to have come from the treasury of the abbey church of Saint Jean-des-Vignes in Soissons (now in the Victoria and Albert Museum, London). Contemporary with the great mid-XIIIth-century creations in stone (Bourges Cathedral jube, Sainte-Chapelle), it features the same classical restraint in the treatment of the high-relief figures, preferring a balanced narrative to active drama. It represents one of the earliest examples of Parisian Gothic ivorywork that was to dominate other centres of production for over a century.

156 Head of a king

Paris, pre-1258
Stone
H 40 cm; L 30 cm; D 23 cm
Notre-Dame de Paris, portal of the north transept
Gift of the Banque Française du Commerce Extérieur, 1980; Cl. 23127

The portal of the north transept was erected by Jean de Chelles and consecrated to the Virgin, whose statue still features on the trumeau. But the attendant statues on the embrasures did not survive the Revolution. According to former descriptions, statues of the Three Wise Men stood on the left of the Virgin, and the head of a king

156

157

found in 1977 seems to have belonged to this group. The same fine workmanship links this head to the statue on the trumeau, while a stylistic elegance and mannerism mark a break with the monumental sculpture of the beginning of the century.

157 St. Stephen

Paris, post-1258
Stone
H 125 cm
Notre-Dame de Paris, portal of the south transept
Discovered in 1839; attributed in 1843; reinv. in 1912; Cl. 18646

The portal on the south transept façade was completed by Pierre de Montreuil and dedicated to St. Stephen, Notre-Dame's first patron saint, whose martyrdom is illustrated on the tympanum. The statue of St. Stephen stood with his back to the trumeau, flanked on each side by six apostles, in the recesses, and by six martyrs, in the angles. Three of them have been identified as St. Denis, St. Rustic and St. Eleuthère, clad in dalmatics and chasubles, and carrying their skulls.

The movement discernible in some of the drapery enhances the effect of light and shade, and situates most of these statues in the mannerist style of Parisian sculpture of the last half of the XIIIth century. Other saints, including St. Stephen, belong to the mid-XIIIth-century period of Parisian classicism.

158 Adam

Paris, circa 1260
Painted stone
H 200 cm
Notre-Dame de Paris, back of the south transept façade
Storerooms of Saint-Denis; attributed in 1887; Cl. 11657

The statue was originally found on the back of the south transept façade with its counterpart Eve, framing the figure of

Christ at the Last Judgement. From an iconographical viewpoint, they were a continuation of the jube decor dedicated to the Passion of Christ and the Judgement. Despite the restoration it has undergone, which mainly involved the lower part of the legs and the right arm, whose hand once held an apple, this statue of Adam has retained an incredible freshness. With a *contraposto* of its own, it is one of the finest Gothic nudes that testifies to the victory of humanism, immediately mirrored on the façade of Rheims Cathedral and which was to act as a stimulus for all artistic production.

159 Altarpiece from Saint-Germer-de-Fly

Parisian region, 1259-1267
Stone
L 376 cm; H 68 cm
Abbey of Saint-Germer-de-Fly, Lady Chapel
Sent by Boeswilwald in 1846; reinv. in 1912; Cl.18749

The altarpiece used to be in the Lady Chapel of the church of Saint-Germer-de-Fly, built under the abbacy of Pierre de Wesoncourt (1259-1272) and consecrated by the Bishop of Beauvais, Guillaume de Grez, in 1267. The rectangular shape raised in the middle had already been found in the altarpieces of Saint-Denis. The principal Crucifixion scene is surrounded by the Church and the Synagogue, St. Peter and St. Paul, the Annunciation and the Visitation. The last four figures at each end of the altarpiece relate to episodes in the life of St. Germer or St. Ouen, Bishop of Rouen, who may be depicted on the extreme left, next to a healing scene. Two scenes from the life of St. Germer or Edward the Confessor are carved on the right.

The altarpiece is stylistically similar to sculptures in the transept of Notre-Dame. Executed in Parisian limestone, it would appear to be from a workshop of the same origin.

158

159 (detail)

160 **Head of the funeral effigy of Jeanne de Toulouse**

Paris region, post-1271
Stone
H 24.5 cm; W 24.5 cm; D 9 cm
Abbey church of Gercy; (now Varennes-Jarcy, Essonne)
Acq. 1971; Cl. 22863

This female mask, whose face is partially hidden by the headband and chinpiece of her veil, comes from the gisant of Jeanne de Toulouse, who was buried in the abbey that she and her husband, Alphonse de Poitiers, had founded at Gercy. Jeanne de Toulouse, daughter of Raymond VII,

Count of Toulouse, had married one of St. Louis' brothers in 1236. When the couple died without leaving an heir in 1271, the Crown took possession of their immense estate covering the whole of south-west France.

The King commissioned one of his sculptors to execute her tomb. He must have been an important Parisian artist of the second half of the XIIIth century who contemplated the portals of Notre-Dame's transept before creating a work of great purity and charm.

160

161 Triptych

Paris, end of XIIIth century
Ivory
L 32 cm; H 28 cm
Church of Saint-Sulpice (Tarn)
Gift of the church of Saint-Sulpice, 1893;
Cl.13101

On opening the movable side panels, six scenes from the Childhood and Passion of Christ are visible, in a two-tiered composition rigorously organised within the architectural decor. At the bottom, the Virgin and Child (missing) between two angels are flanked, on the left, by the Three Kings and, on the right, by a Presentation in the Temple scene. On the top, the Crucifixion, with Longin and Stephaton, is framed by a Road to Calvary, on the left, and a Descent from the Cross on the right.

With the combination of figures in bold relief on the thick central ivory panel and the flattened, more graphic figures of the side panels, this triptych foresaw the increase in devotional polyptychs during the XIVth century, when the same recurrent themes and a growing tendency toward slender forms would be found.

162 Angel

Paris region, post-1297
Stone
H 100 cm
Poissy, priory of St. Louis
Acq. 1987; Cl. 23292

Angels in the round, holding instruments of the Passion or blowing trumpets, must have accompanied the scene of Christ at the Last Judgement. They may have perched on columns around one of the altars in the church of the Dominican priory of Saint-Louis at Poissy, founded by King Philip the Fair to commemorate the birthplace of his grandfather, Louis IX, who was

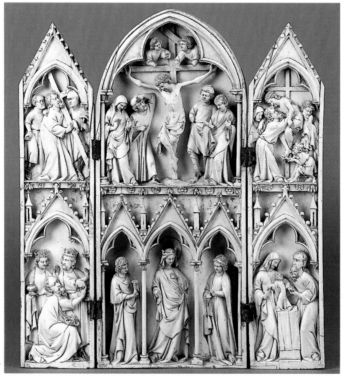

161

162

Palais de la Cité in Paris, sculpture had become an excellent political weapon. This royal commission went to leading artists who would steer the monumental Parisian style of the second half of the XIIIth century towards the more delicate, refined artform perpetuated by XIVth-century courtly art.

163 **Mirror case**

Paris, circa 1300
Ivory
Diam. 14 cm
Du Sommerard collection; Cl. 404

Everyday objects made out of ivory were extremely popular in the XIVth century. Caskets, knife handles, writing tablets and mirror cases were produced in great quantities to satisfy a fashion-conscious aristocracy. The two sides of the mirror cases fitted into each other when turned, concealing the mirror within. The outsides were often decorated with scenes of courtly love. The Musée de Cluny's exhibit, known as "The Assembly", is remarkable for its precocity, its large size and its iconography. The king and queen sit enthroned, trampling the dragon and the lion underfoot, while an angel emerging from clouds

canonised in 1297. In addition to these angel figures, the richly sculpted decor depicted St. Louis and his wife, Marguerite of Provence, with six of their children (the Museum possesses the statue of Pierre d'Alençon). This project intended to glorify the royal family, at a time when, with the series of tombs in Saint-Denis commissioned by St. Louis and the kings in the

163

seems to designate the king or the shield above him. This may represent a French king and his followers (Philip the Fair, Philip V or even Louis IX), but could also refer to the biblical King of Solomon and the Queen of Sheba.

The refined workmanship denotes a work worthy of the court, in a style similar to the Poissy sculptures commissioned by Philip the Fair.

164   Chessman: the king

Scandinavia or northern Europe, early XIVth century
Whalebone (?)
H 7.8 cm; L 6 cm
Stein Donation, 1885; Cl. 11285

Chess was introduced to the West from India and Persia around the year 1000, and despite Church disapproval, rapidly became a favourite pastime among the upper classes. Complete games from this period are rare, but church treasuries and archeological digs often yield individual pieces, like this seated king and its matching piece, a hunter blowing an oliphant, our present-day bishop. The king holds a sword, while, to his right, a figure throws an enemy to the ground, and, to his left, a

man plays the bagpipes. Two soldiers appear to be on guard behind the throne. It is probably made from whalebone, which would denote a Nordic origin.

Guillaume de Nourriche

165   Apostle

Paris, 1319-1324
Stone
H 171 cm; W 51 cm
Paris, church of the Saint-Jacques-aux-Pèlerins Hospice
Attributed in 1852; reinv. in 1912; Cl. 18759

Construction of the huge Saint-Jacques-aux-Pèlerins Hospice began in 1319, to shelter pilgrims on their way to Santiago de Compostela, and included a richly decorated church. Two sculptors, Robert de Lannoy and Guillaume de Nourriche, executed a figure of Christ together with an apostolic assembly, a theme borrowed from the Sainte-Chapelle (*154*). Examination of hospice accounts and the five remaining statues from the cycle has indicated the role played by each artist. From 1319-1324, Guillaume worked on two statues of apostles, while Robert executed four, completing the series in 1326-1327.

One of the statues is easily distinguished from the four others by its more incisive style and expressive face. It was probably the work of Guillaume de Nourriche, whose name may be a distortion of Norwich, the possible English hometown of our artist who settled and was known in Paris from 1297 onwards.

164

166 **Virgin and Child**

Lorraine, 1325-1350
Stone
H 91 cm; W 30 cm; D 22
Timbal Legacy, 1881; Cl. 18944

A favourite theme of XIVth-century sculpture, statues of the Virgin and Child were found all over Christendom. In France alone, there are more than a thousand specimens in existence from this period, which offers a privileged field of observation in artistic creation and enables the transmission of forms to be traced.

166

165

The Lorraine Virgins, like those in the Museum and the Cathedral of Saint-Dié, conform to a similar stocky silhouette and are all veiled and crowned, while the Child reading a breviary is an unusual detail. The Lorraine centre would be one of the main relays between the thriving courtly art of the Ile-de-France and the Rhineland region around Cologne.

167 Bust-reliquary of a companion of St. Ursula

Cologne, circa 1340
Polychrome wood (lime tree)
H 47.5 cm
Acq. 1885; Cl 11306

The cult of St. Ursula and the eleven thousand virgins was enormously popular throughout Christendom in the XIVth century. A regular trade in relics, and consequently in reliquaries, sprang up (**174**). In Cologne itself, the sacristy of the Church of St. Ursula contains countless examples. These reliquaries formed an integral part of Cologne sculptors' production between 1325 and 1350. The busts were frequently cut off at the shoulders and sometimes at the waist. The front of the bust featured decorative openwork, while the top of the head could be removed to see the martyr's skull.

The Museum's bust bears witness to the successive updating of medieval works. The reliquary was originally painted in very natural colours; its present state results from a radical intervention, doubtless during the baroque period, when the hair and vestimentary ornaments were gilded, while the face and smooth parts of the bust were silvered. The silver has now blackened, but the idea behind this transformation may have been to recall the brilliance of reliquaries in precious metals.

168 Doctor

Bologna, circa 1340
Marble
H 81.5 cm; W 54 cm
Acq. 1884; Cl. 11115

From the second half of the XIIIth century onwards, tombs of Doctors from the University of Bologna, one of the most prestigious in Europe and specialised in law, were frequent. From the start of the XIVth to the mid-XVth century, the representation of a Doctor teaching his students from the rostrum was predominant in funereal art, an early example of the primacy of the "worldly", or earthly, aspect over that of the anticipated entry of the dead into Paradise. The hieratical figure conveys the elitism of a much-honoured, somewhat withdrawn social group.

167

168

Workshop of Jaume Cascalls

169 **Mourner**

Southern Catalonia, second half of XIVth
century
Alabaster
H 30 cm
Gift of Guy Ladrière, 1986; Cl. 23251

169

Figures in mourning, either individual or
grouped around tombs, were very popular
in the XIVth century. The theme was
widespread, even before Claus Sluter
added a hitherto unknown dramatic dimension to Philip the Bold's tomb in the Carthusian monastery of Champmol. The
style, size and medium, a Gerona alabaster,
of this mourner are very similar to those
adorning the tombs executed by the workshop of sculptor Jaume Cascalls (active

around 1345-1380) in the Abbey of Poblet.
The artist replaced Aloi de Montbrai in
this vast undertaking launched by King
Peter IV that was to transform this Cistercian monastery into a Pantheon of the
Kings of Aragon.
As the Cascalls' workshop also produced
other tombs between Tarragona and
Lerida, the provenance of this mourner
dating from the second half of the XIVth
century can be extended to the whole of
southern Catalonia.

170

Annunciation scene. The subject of the Archangel Gabriel announcing to the Virgin she had been chosen to be the mother of God was extremely frequent in Italy at the end of the Middle Ages. At some point, the statues of the Virgin and the angel were separated, but it may one day be possible to identify the Virgin among individually displayed works.

The angel is normally attributed to the workshop of Nino Pisano, one of a famous dynasty of Tuscan sculptors practising between 1349 and 1368. The Museum's angel may have been based on a marble Annunciation group in the Church of Santa Caterina in Pisa, as other complete or partial Annunciation groups, like the one in the Louvre and the Montefoscoli group recently attributed to the same artist, the Master of the Annunciation of Montefoscoli. Common to all is a sense of restraint and a certain classicism typical of Nino and his workshop, marvellously expressed in these large sculpted groups, whose numerous, skilfully painted creations in wood rivalled marble sculpture.

171 **Tombstone of Jean de Sathanay**

Paris, 1360
Stone
H 313 cm; W 155 cm
Paris, Cluny College Chapel
Séguin Donation, 1852; reinv. in 1912;
Cl. 18822

Floors in medieval churches, cloisters and other religious edifices were often covered in memorial stones. The majority of these slabs, dating back to the early XIIIth century, were simply engraved, so as not to cause obstruction. Some of them are true masterpieces of graphic art, as is the tombstone of Jean de Sathanay, advisor to the King and Abbot of Ferrières-en-Gâtinais, who died in 1360 in Cluny College, the refuge to which he fled at the end of his life to escape the misfortunes of the Hundred Years' War. He was buried in the College chapel, near the present-day Place de la Sorbonne. The slab is in stone, but the head, hands, crozier and coats of arms

Master of the Annunciation
of Montefoscoli

170 **Angel of the Annunciation**

Tuscany, 1350-1375
Polychrome wood
H 177 cm
Timbal Legacy, 1881; Cl. 12560

This tall figure of an angel was originally accompanied by a statue of the Virgin in an

171

172 Presentation in the Temple

Paris, circa 1370-1380
Marble
H 63 cm; W 45 cm; D 14 cm
Du Sommerard Collection; reinv. in 1912;
Cl. 18849

The scene, treated in two blocks whose central part is a modern restoral, attests to the moment when the respectful old man Simeon recognises the child in swaddling clothes, delicately presented by the Virgin, as Christ. A picturesque note is added by the servant. The sculpture was probably meant to fill the background of an altarpiece which may have included an angel (now in the Metropolitan Museum, New York). The exceptional quality of both the composition that conveys a rare sense of space and the psychological sensitivity or detailed craftsmanship denotes the work of a great artist, such as André Beauneveu or Jean de Liège. Parallels between the treatment of this Presentation in the Temple and works stylistically close to Jean de Liège, like the head of the funeral effigy of

172

were inlaid with marble. The defunct is represented with hands clasped in prayer, under an arcade flanked by two rows of bishops, abbots and monks standing in superposed, rectangular recesses, while his identity is revealed by an epitaph around the edge of the tombstone.

Bonne de France (Mayer van den Bergh Museum, Antwerp), cannot however eliminate one of the many Parisian artists whose works, although unidentified, are recorded.

173 St. John the Evangelist

Paris, circa 1370-1380
Marble
H 115 cm; W 38 cm; D 20 cm
Longchamp Abbey (?)
Storerooms of Saint-Denis; reinv. in 1912;
Cl. 19255

Diversity was rife at the end of the XIVth century. Artistic production did not only include highly refined works. Others of a stronger temperament existed, in which the artist strived to express a certain restlessness, rather than search for the perfect line or the finest polish. The emaciated facial features, vehement drapery and instable pose of this figure of St. John, the young apostle, are thus in total contrast with the more ethereal and serene statues attributed to the great names of sculpture during this period.

Angelo di Nalduccio (?)

174 Bust-reliquary of St. Mabilla

Siena, circa 1370-1380
Polychrome wood
H 46 cm; W 33 cm; D 22 cm
Delange Coll.
Acq. 1857; Cl. 2624

An inscription on the base identifies this saint as one of St. Ursula's eleven thousand maiden companions in Cologne. The bust-reliquary contains the martyr's skull. The hair and clothes have retained their original colouring, whereas the flesh tints have been slightly retouched. The facial features remain marked by the same grave, disturbing determination as in a similar angel of the Annunciation (Museo Civico e d'Arte Sacra, Montalcino) dating from 1370 and signed by Angelo. It may refer to Angelo di Nalduccio, a Sienese painter (1343-1389), whose activity as a sculptor is however unproven. The sculpted forms of these

173

174

175 (detail)

works have been reduced to the essential and detail is rendered through polychromy alone.

Three other busts of St. Ursula's companions, one in San Gimignano (Museo Civico) and two in Florence (Santa Maria Novella) attest to the widespread cult to the Cologne martyrs in the XIVth century (**167**).

Balthazar Embriachi (workshop)

175 **Altarpiece**

> North Italy, pre-1393
> Marquetry and bone
> H 130 cm; W 75 cm
> Dijon, Carthusian monastery of
> Champmol;
> Cretet Coll., Bertholomey Coll.
> Acq. 1849; reinv. in 1908; Cl. 17051

This small altarpiece, called the *Oratory of the Duchesses of Burgundy*, comes from the

176

Carthusian monastery of Champmol, near Dijon. It was commissioned with another piece by the Duke and paid for in 1393. It was made in the Florentine workshop of Balthazar Embriachi, who specialised in the production of different-sized altarpieces and caskets, composed of carved bone plaquettes, juxtaposed to create religious or secular scenes, arranged in rows and framed by wooden and tinted bone marquetry. These creations were hugely successful; the workshop was transferred to Venice and continued its activity until 1433.

The style of the sculptures and the decoration on the uprights may be compared to contemporary parts of the Duomo in Florence, and to certain features of the belltower and door of the Mandorla. The loss, replacement and rearrangement of the plaquettes may limit one's appreciation of the whole work that was initially devoted to the life and Passion of Christ.

176 **Road to Calvary**

Paris, circa 1400
Polychrome wood (walnut)
H 45 cm; W 48 cm; TH 13 cm
Inv. in 1907, Cl. 16781 (Simeon);
reinv. in 1923, Cl. 20638
(five other figures)

The fact that this ornamental sculpture has been attributed to various workshops in Paris or Flanders demonstrates the international nature of art around 1400. Decades of fruitful exchanges between different artistic centres of the West saw the evolution of a generalised refinement in style. The elegance of the curved lines, the rich colour range and predominant gold take nothing away from the uneasy tension of the narrative, a prologue to XVth-century realism. The play of hands on the arms of the Cross, the exchange of looks and the drapery pulled over the head, or merely suggested, intensify the distress of Christ's companions, caught in the drama of the Passion.

177 Head of a funeral effigy

Tournai (?), circa 1400
Tournai stone
H 32 cm; W 23 cm; TH 10 cm
Acq. 1992; Cl. 23412

This head of a mature bearded man comes from a gisant executed in Tournai stone, a carboniferous limestone, polished until black and lustrous, which pinpoints the work's origin to one of the workshops around Tournai, in Belgium, specialised in funerary sculpture. Their distribution area covered the Scheldt valley, Flanders, Artois and western Hainault.

Decorative headbands being reserved for high-ranking figures, this head obviously belonged to a princely tomb, as in Louvain, Bruges, Lille (Counts of Flanders) or Valenciennes (Counts of Hainault).

The hairstyle and forked beard confirm a dating of around 1400, consistent with the expression of the strong facial features, whose wrinkles belie a nascent realism without undermining the sovereign's calm authority.

177

178

178 Virgin and Child

Paris, circa 1400
Polychrome stone
H 138 cm
Paris, Abbey of St. Victor (?)
Acq. 1850; Cl. 18764

Towards 1400 art reached the heights of refinement and elegance, thus crowning one of the main European trends of XIVth-century creation, so much so that one might speak of an International Gothic

179

style. The French counterpart, or even prototype of the fine central European madonnas, this Virgin, supposed to have originated in the former Parisian Abbey of St. Victor, adopts a graceful pose, while the lateral folds of her coat falling symmetrically are drawn tighter around her ankles to add lightness and momentum. The Child's eagerness to take the breast only intensifies his mother's contrasting regal aspect.

179 Leaf from a diptych

Middle Rhine, circa 1400
Ivory
H 15 cm; W 11 cm
Constantin Legacy, 1881; Cl. 10904

The other half of this diptych depicts the Virgin with St. Peter and St. Paul and is in the Museum of Langres. With the Crucifixion scene of this leaf, it formed a devotional diptych that the faithful could easily carry around. Stylistically close to a diptych kept in the Abbey of Kremsmünster (Austria), this ivory testifies to the same picturesque artform, yet is richer in architectural decor than others, while its figures are more expressive than those from Pari-

sian workshops. These pieces have been attributed to the Middle Rhineland through analogies with sculptures from the Mainz region.

180 Virgin

Western Prussia, circa 1400
Polychrome wood (lime tree)
L 45 cm (open); H 20 cm; TH 11 cm
Haas Donation, 1890; Cl. 12060

A special feature of this Virgin and Child is that it has two panels that open into a kind of triptych illustrating the Throne of Grace, or God the Father holding Christ on the Cross (the ivory Christ is more recent), and the Virgin of Mercy, whose outstretched arms protect the men and women painted on the back of the panels. Among them one may notice crowned figures, a bishop and, on the far right, a Teutonic Knight in his distinctive long white coat stamped with a cross, probably the donator.

180

181

This sort of openable statuette of the Virgin combining three iconographical themes was peculiar to western Prussia under Teutonic domination. Other existing examples have the same origin and express certain theological concepts of the era. Johannes Marienwerder (1343-1417) spoke of the triple birth of Jesus: through the Father without the Mother (the Throne of Grace), the Mother without the Father (the closed Virgin) and in the heart of mankind (sheltered here by the merciful Virgin).

181 **The Lamentation of Christ**

Burgundy, 1400-1450
Polychrome wood (oak and walnut)
Total H 82 cm
Acq. 1988; Cl. 23311

Helped by Mary-Magdalen and St. John, the Virgin, in the centre, holds the inert body of Christ that has just been taken down from the Cross. The pathos of the scene, equal to that of the Pietà, echoes the morbid piety of a population sorely tried

182

182   Virgin and Child

Dijon, 1425-1450
Stone H 97 cm
Burgundy, portal of the Sainte-Apollinaire
Castle, near Dijon
Timbal Donation, 1881; reinv. in 1912;
Cl. 18926

Burgundy was a major XVth-century artistic centre under the patronage of Philip the Bold. Numerous artists are recorded as having worked there and their distribution was widespread.

The Virgin from the Castle of Sainte-Apollinaire, like the one from the collegiate church of Auxonne, is distinguished by the heaviness of the drapery whose ample folds mask the broad figure, in a style long attributed to Claus de Werve, but which would be more prudent to leave anonymous. At any rate, the work displays the originality of Burgundy art, whose impact on Western art would be felt until the end of the Middle Ages.

183   Epitaph of Nicolas Flamel

Paris, 1418
Stone
H 56 cm; W 40 cm
Paris, Church of Saint-Jacques-de-la-Boucherie
Gift of the City of Paris, 1845;
reinv. in 1912; Cl. 18823

by the misfortunes of time, war, famine and epidemics. The piece was small enough to be a devotional object used at home for private worship by individual religious members or laymen.

The sculpture is stylistically close to major works of Burgundy art that evolved in the Dijon court of the Dukes of Valois, who employed the greatest sculptors of the period. Despite its size, this work retains a monumental quality and has been attributed to the associates of Claus de Werve, who replaced his uncle Claus Sluter as head of the ducal workshops.

The tomb of Nicolas Flamel (circa 1330-1418), in the Church of Saint-Jacques-de-la-Boucherie, was identified from this engraved ledger. A sworn scribe at the University of Paris, who owed his fame to his supposed skills as an alchemist, the recumbent figure of his naked corpse is depicted in a state of decomposition. This was current practise at the end of the Middle Ages, when the misfortunes of time had given rise to a morbid piety confirmed in the epitaph, "From earth I came and to earth return, I commit my soul to thee Jesus who pardons all sin."

The prayer uttered by the deceased, "Lord God, I trusted in thy mercy," is offered to Christ at the Last Judgement seen at the top of the tombstone, between the sun and the moon, holding the cruciferous orb beside St. Peter and St. Paul. Nicolas' works of charity on behalf of Parisian churches and hospitals are opportunely mentioned before the traditional invitation to pray for the dead.

184 **Annunciation**

Nottingham, XVth century
Alabaster
H 41.5 cm; W 26 cm
Du Sommerard collection; reinv. in 1912;
Cl. 19343

The Virgin on her knees in front of a desk, under a baldaquin, makes a frightened gesture as she turns round towards the angel who greets her. The dove of the Holy Spirit descends from Heaven, where God the Father is featured holding the cruciferous orb. This alabaster plaque was no doubt part of an altarpiece that included

184

183

other scenes from the life of the Virgin and the Childhood of Christ. These alabaster sculptures were almost mass-produced in the XIVth and XVth centuries in Nottingham, due to the proximity of vast quarries. They were exported throughout Christendom as far as the Mediterranean.
Although their execution was often unfeeling and repetitive, the occasional work revealed true craftsmanship, as in this plaque where the delicate cutting and fragility of the opaline medium are enhanced by subtle polychromy.

185 **Head of Christ**

Franconia, circa 1470
Polychrome wood (lime tree)
H 32 cm; W 18 cm; TH 13 cm
Coignet Legacy, 1919; Cl. 20270

Parallels drawn with better preserved and documented crucifixes on display in Würzburg (Neumünster) and Nuremberg (Germanisches Nationalmuseum), have solved

185

187

the enigma of this analogous head of Christ, which combines a synthetic treatment of volume with realistic details: wrinkles, half-open mouth, thin nose, accentuated by the still visible polychromy and a wig that covered the broad skull.

This work belonged to Franconian art of around 1470, and issued from another trend than the Christs with the typical elongated silhouettes of Veit Stoss and Tilman Riemenschneider's workshops, being closer to the more expressive style of Hans Multscher and his associates that sometimes verged on grimacing realism.

186

Master Arnt

186 **Altarpiece**

> Kalkar, Lower Rhine, circa 1483
> Polychrome painted wood
> H 97 cm; W 45 cm (closed)
> Soltykoff Coll.
> Acq. 1861; Cl. 3269

This small altarpiece contained a drawer where devotional objects could be kept. The sculpture inside the casing depicts the Lamentation of Christ at the foot of the Cross, a theme very much in keeping with the uneasy, morbid piety prevalent in the Late Middle Ages. Scenes of the Nativity and the Adoration of the Magi are painted on the exterior of the side panels, while six episodes from Christ's Passion are featured on the inside.

The presence of the donor, a Carthusian kneeling in prayer, and that of the town of Kranenburg, near Nijmegen, in the background of the Adoration of the Magi, may pinpint the altarpiece's origin to the house acquired there by the Carthusians of Roermund in 1483.

Attributed to Arnt of Kalkar, an artist who worked on the stalls in the Church of the Minorites at Clèves in 1474 and renowned for his key work, the altarpiece of St. George in Kalkar, this sculpture, which has retained its original polychromy, reflects the impact made by a style inspired from Rogier Van Der Weyden on the Lower Rhine region.

187 **Altarpiece**

> Utrecht, last third of XVth century
> Terracotta
> H 95 cm; L 229 cm; D 15 cm
> Chapel of the former St. Lambert Priory, appertaining to the Abbey of Bec-Hellouin (Eure)
> Acq. 1861; Cl. 3201

The moulded terracotta sculptures of this altarpiece illustrating the Marriage of the Virgin, the Nativity and the Adoration of the Magi were mass-produced in Utrecht, according to documents and archeological evidence. Moreover, they are stylistically analogous with sculptures executed in this Dutch town around 1470 in the sphere of Adrian Van Wesel's activity. Many sculptures were exported in the same way as the wooden altarpieces from Antwerp (**193**). Similar terracotta altarpieces are thus found in the Netherlands, Denmark

and Spain, while the vast majority are preserved in Normandy, original home of the
Museum's exhibit.

188 **Altarpiece**

Champagne, 1484
Polychrome limestone
H 190 cm; L 326 cm
Provins, Cordelier convent
Gift of the town of Provins, 1861;
Cl. 18751

This large altarpiece was found among the
ruins of the Cordelier convent in Provins in
the XIXth century. The inscription running along the bottom reveals both the
date, 1484, and the purchaser's name, Jean
de Bierne.
Scenes of the Annunciation, the Nativity,
the Resurrection and Pentecost are featured on either side of the central Crucifixion
scene (the donor is found at the foot of the
Cross). Despite its mutilated state, the
altarpiece attests to the work's exceptional
quality. The finely wrought sculpture is
enhanced by the polychrome of the figures,
background and sumptuous decor with

daises set under the wide continuous
moulding that accentuates the altarpiece's
contours and whose groove is adorned with
a procession of seraphims.

189 **Choir stalls**

Beauvais, late XVth century
Wood
H 87 cm
Saint-Lucien of Beauvais
Storerooms of Saint-Denis
Acq. 1970; Cl. 22859

The choir stalls from the former Abbey of
Saint-Lucien in Beauvais, together with
those from Amiens Cathedral, constitute
one of the most important groups by
Picardy hutch-makers of the Late Middle
Ages. They were commissioned by Abbot
Antoine Du Bois (1492-1500), who is
depicted on one of the reveals in front of
his patron saint, a counterpart to St. Peter
sending St. Lucien, St. Maxien and St.
Julien (**102**) to evangelise the inhabitants of
Beauvais. A lively spirit animates the carvings on the arm-rests and above all the
misericords, those small projections on the

188

189

bottom of the hinged seat that, when the latter was turned up during services, supported the standing monks. The sculptors' keen sense of observation of everyday life may be seen in their representation of various trades, while the clownish, almost irreligious scenes display a vivid imagination.

190 St. Mary-Magdalen

Brussels, late XVth century
Wood (oak)
H 97 cm; W 36 cm; TH 24 cm
Debruge-Duménil Coll.
Acq. 1850; Cl. 1851

This charming, almost profane Mary-Magdalen is depicted with her conventional symbol, the pot of perfume meant to embalm the body of Christ, whom she believed she would find at the Sepulchre. The saint's elegant hairstyle, with plaits twisted around a bonnet before falling on her shoulders, contrasts with the relative simplicity of her clothing and general appearance.

Together with another statue of Mary-Magdalen (Musée du Cinquantenaire, Brussels), it has thus been compared to works by late XVth-century Brussels sculptors, specialised in devotional statuary and altarpieces, like the one of St. George completed by Jan Borreman in 1493 for the chapel of Notre-Dame-du-Dehors of Louvain (Musée du Cinquantenaire, Brussels). Exact parallels with the choir stalls of

192

190

191

Saint-Sulpice in Diest, dated 1491-1493, have established a similar dating for this Mary-Magdalen.

191   **St. Barbara**

Champagne, early XVIth century
Polychrome limestone
H 80 cm
Acq. 1870; Cl. 18786

The martyr's palm and the tower sum up the legend of St. Barbara, who converted to Christianity after being locked in a tower by her father. During her imprisonment, she had a third window made in the adjoining bathroom wall, to symbolise the Holy Trinity. Her father, whom she tried in vain to convert, condemned her to death. She managed to escape, but was finally caught and tortured, before being decapitated by her father himself, who was then struck dead by lightning. St. Barbara, invoked against the plague and sudden death, was a favourite intercessor in the Late Middle Ages, as is seen from the numerous devotional statues of her that remain today. This tall, lithe, graceful young girl with such an elegant head-dress is one of the most charming statues from the thriving Champagne centre at the dawn of the Renaissance.

192   **Altarpiece of the Passion**

Netherlands and Champagne (?), early XVIth century
Polychrome wood and painted panels
H 200 cm; L 248 cm
Champdeuil (Seine-et-Marne)
Gift of the Commune of Champdeuil, 1861; Cl. 20635

Scenes of the Passion cover the central part of this large altarpiece, with a swarm of figures, some of whom have the typical coarse expressions of sculpture from the southern Netherlands. The side panels that could be folded over the central part are painted back and front. On the outside, the very incomplete paintings depicted the Annunciation between two ecclesiastic saints, one of whom presented the donor. Four half-length portraits of the Evangelists were featured underneath. On the interior of each side panel were six apostles, each one above a bust of a prophet painted along the bottom. A certain Lucas Lois signed the panels three times, but nothing is known of him.
The provenance of the paintings, very different in style from the sculptures, might be closer to the altarpiece's former home, in Champdeuil, near Melun.

Jan de Molder

193 Altarpiece of the Blessed Sacrament

Antwerp, 1513-1514
Polychrome wood
H 228 cm; L 205 cm; D 33 cm
Averbode, Abbey of the Premonstrants
Du Sommerard collection; Cl. 240

This altarpiece, whose painted side panels no longer exist, was delivered, at Easter in 1514, to the Averbode Abbey in Brabant, to adorn the altar of the Blessed Sacrament

Its destination thus dictated an iconography relevant to the Eucharist. In the centre, the Adoration of the Host, presented in a monstrance held by two angels wearing dalmatics, is depicted under the scene of the Mass of St. Gregory, during which Christ miraculously appeared on the altar, at the Pope's request. Featured on the left is the Meeting of Abraham and Melchisedec: the priest-king of Salem, represented here as a Bishop, leaves the city to bless Abraham after his combat. The Last Supper can be seen on the right. With another large altarpiece and nume

193

194

rous individual fragments, the Averbode altarpiece illustrates the intense activity of the Antwerp sculptors' workshops, in the late XVth-early XVIth centuries, authenticated by the mark of a cut hand, taken from the parochial arms and branded on the wood. The works of Jan de Molder were typical of this artform abounding in scenes and figures that made up picturesque, sometimes exotic, always delectable compositions within skilful architectural decors.

Hans Leinberger workshop

194 **Family of St. Anne**

Bavaria, 1510-1520
Polychrome wood
L 100 cm; H 94 cm
Acq. 1987; Cl. 23310

St. Anne, mother of the Virgin, is found holding her daughter, depicted as an ado-lescent, on her right, and the Infant Jesus on her left knee. The theme of the Family of St. Anne highlighted the Immaculate Conception of the Virgin and made a late, somewhat successful appearance at the end of the Middle Ages (**121**).

The work recalls, on a slightly inferior level, the art of Hans Leinberger, a sculptor active in Bavaria between 1510 and 1530, whose style had considerable impact in the region. Certain features of this great artist's work may be seen in St. Anne's heavy face and the thick folds broken by the creases of the material, or falling in extravagant whorls, which echo the Virgins in the Moosburg or St. Martin of Landshut altarpieces, the culmination of baroque tendencies in Germanic sculpture of the Late Middle Ages.

Textiles

Fabrics, embroideries, tapestries

Artistic fabrics

The manufacture of materials is closely linked to the civilisation that produces them. Abstract or figurative motifs add a significative, iconographical dimension. Since the birth of mankind, figuration has been a determinant factor that acquires a special meaning when used for demonstration: fabric is meant to be seen, to be noticed, to be admired. The role played by the medium - wool, silk, metal - is as important as that of the design and colour. Material's irresistible charm reached special heights in the Middle Ages, due to the diversity of techniques, the resolute distribution of the finished product and the prevalent desire to acquire works. From a simple question of the warp and the weft evolved a vast field abounding in potential. The creation of fabric resulted from both technical and artistic imagination: brocaded silk, brocade, brocatelle, damask, lampas, velvet were just a few. The beauty of the words becomes an evocation of an even richer reality when the material submits to movement, deep in shadow or resplendent in the light. The National Museum of the Middle Ages' extensive collection in this domain cannot be displayed in its entirety, due to lack of space and for security reasons. Our only resource is to exhibit works in rotation, our aim being to combine both presentation and preservation.

Alain Erlande-Brandenburg

Coptic textiles

Territorial and chronological fluctuations have made it difficult to pinpoint the areas of Coptic production, even today. Although closely linked to the Mediterranean, the complex nature of its civilisations cannot be reduced to a single site: it remains as vague as the word Copt itself. From a chronological viewpoint, the production can no doubt be placed between the Roman conquest and the Arab invasion of 640. Indeed, it extends well beyond that date, perhaps even up to the XIIth century. Two types of production have been distinguished after technical analysis: the first specialised in silk fabrics, the second in linen and wools. It is hard to be precise concerning the latter, more prolific production: the textiles came from clandestine finds outside of any archeological context; their chronology can thus rest only on aesthetic criteria based on the mistaken idea of an evolution of forms. The Museum's collections follow the same criteria: all the exhibits were either personally donated by the owner or given by the State. Certain textiles are said to have come from the Antinoë excavations undertaken by A. Gay, but the lack of archeological evidence demands some degree of prudence.

195

195 Jason and Medea

Egypt, IVth-Vth century (?)
Linen and wool
Diam. 7 cm
Antinoë (?)
Claudius Côte Bequest, 1961; CL 22813

This tapestry medallion most likely recalls an episode from the story of Jason and Medea: in the sacred wood of Ares, they attempt to seize the Golden Fleece, guarded by a monstrous serpent. This figuration is rare in textiles and was probably taken from subsequent copies of a prototype.

196

Textiles

196 **Hairnet**

Egypt, Vth century (?)
Linen, wool
H 32 cm; W 70 cm (approx)
Probably Antinoë
State Gift, 1905; CL 17576

The morphology of the object has determined its function, an assymetrical female head-dress (?).

Oriental textiles

An iconoclastic decree of 754 forbade all figurative images in textile techniques throughout the Byzantine Empire. This ban was probably not respected, for it would have endangered an ancient and perfectly mastered production, manifest in the quality of the works, despite chronological uncertainty. At any rate, trade with Europe remained intensive, though not necessarily connected, as is frequently thought, to the cult of relics. These precious fabrics, technical marvels scintillating with colour, were often found unexpectedly in tombs or reliquaries.

197 **Quadriga**

Constantinople, VIIIth century
Silk
H 75 cm; L 72.5 cm
Aachen
De Vielcastel Coll.
Acq. 1850; CL 13289

This fragment of samite, completed by others kept in the treasury of Aachen, was found in Charlemagne's reliquary. Tradition wrongly claimed that it had wrapped the Emperor's body. It illustates victory at the hippodrome, an allusion to imperial triumph. The quadriga, driven by a successful charioteer, is typical of VIIIth-century production at the court of Constantinople.

197

Hispano-Moresque fabrics

In Spain, production soared both in quality and quantity. Indications of this include the cultivation of mulberries, introduced to Andalousia in the Xth century, and numerous documents. Massive exportation to Italy began in the IXth century and extended to northern Europe in the XIIth century. Whole consignments of silks and garments in gold brocade or enhanced by gold embroidery left the country.

198

198 Fragment from the shroud of St. Lazarus of Autun

Spain, Almeria (?), early XIth century
Silk and gold thread
H 55 cm; W 29 cm
Autun Cathedral; Claudius Côte Coll.
Anonymous gift [D. David Weill], 1933;
CL 21865

This blue silk shroud shared today between the treasury of Autun Cathedral, the Musée Historique des Tissus in Lyons and our Parisian Museum, presents a series of multilobed medallions surrounding horsemen and female sphinxes. From the inscription an allusion may be made to Abd-al-Malik, conqueror of Sanche Garcia, Count of Castile, giving a 1007 dating. Executed in the south of the peninsula, it resembles contemporary Hispanic production and remains one of Spain's oldest Islamic creations.

199 Fragment from the shroud of St. Sernin of Toulouse

Spain, XIIth century
Silk
H 44 cm; W 23 cm
Basilica of St. Sernin of Toulouse
Acq. 1892; CL 12869

This small fragment was taken from a shroud kept in the treasury of St. Sernin. It was first discovered in 1582, then in 1846, in the reliquary of St. Exupère. The samite features alternate red and yellow medallions on a black background, with large affronté peacocks in their pride either side of a stylised palmette. An inscription meaning "supreme benediction" in Kufic lettering confirms its XIIth-century Hispano-Moresque origin.

199   200

**200 Fragment from the cope
of St. Mesme of Chinon**

Spain (?), XIIth century
Silk
H 16.5 cm; W 36 cm
Chinon, Church of St. Stephen
Gift of the town of Chinon, 1935;
CL 22018

Leopards chained to a tree are featured on
this Hispano-Moresque samite with a blue
background. It comes from a cope still preserved in the Church of St. Stephen in
Chinon and dates from the 1100s.

Italian fabrics

*Italian production cannot be limited to works
that saw the day in XIIth-century Sicily,
however prolific they may have been . An
unrivalled centre of activity grew up around
Roger II (post-1154) in Palermo and its
success throughout Europe led to the creation
of other centres: in Lucca, as early as XIIth
century, then later in Sienna, Venice and
Genoa. Oriental technique was occasionally
combined with an iconography of Western
inspiration.*

201

French fabrics

Even today, little is known about French fabrics; historians have rarely delved into an industry that depended more on individual choice than intensive production. Contrary to what happened in XIIth-century Spain and Italy or XIVth-century England, there were no aspirations to export and hence no centre to impose its technique, colours or designs. Works catalogued today as French sprang from an artistic rather than an industrial concept. Textiles being a means of expression, dazzling analogies with painting have appeared. This may explain why great care has been taken to draw parallels between the most famous works and renowned contemporary artists.

201 Pontifical stocking of Arnaud de Via

Italy, Lucca, XIIIth century
Silk, gold
H 63 cm; L 28 cm
Abbey of Villeneuve-lès-Avignon (Gard)
Gift of the Prefect of Gard, 1867;
CL 8604

Discovered in the XIXth century in the binding of a cartulary at the Abbey of Villeneuve-lès-Avignon, it is said to have belonged to Arnaud de Via, Archbishop of Bayonne, who died in 1331. Adorned with affronté eagles and antelopes, this variegated silk brocade from Lucca has certain details highlighted in gold thread and was a XIIIth-century work transformed into stockings the following century.

202 Corporal case

France (?), mid-XIIIth century
Linen, gold and silk thread
H 18 cm; L 16 cm
Acq. 1852; CL 2159

The corporal case was a sachet used to hold the corporal. St. John the Baptist and the Crucifixion are embroidered in silk and gold thread on either side of the linen drill. From the XIIIth-century iconography, it could possibly be a work of French origin.

202

203

underneath a monk offers a liturgical garment, while at the bottom are Count Manasseh and Countess Ermengarda. At the end of the IXth century, the latter founded the monastery of St. Vivant of Vergy, former home of this exhibit. Although the technique is of English origin, it may have been executed in France in the second half of the XIIIth century.

204 Alms-purse "of the Countess of Bar"

France, XIVth century
Silk, metal thread
H 36 cm; L 32 cm
Abbey of Saint-Mihiel (Meuse)
Acq. 1888; CL 11787

This green silk alms-purse, embroidered with silk and metal thread and adorned with grotesque figures, is a secular work from the second third of the XIVth century. Together with another alms-purse on display (CL 11788), it comes from the Abbey of Saint-Mihiel and is said to have belonged to a Countess of Bar (?).

203 Orphrey of Manasseh and Ermengarda

France (?), end of XIIIth century
Silk, linen, gold thread
H 69 cm; W 28 cm
Monastery of St. Vivant of Vergy (Côte-d'Or); Baudot Coll.
Acq. 1852; CL 2158

This rectangular piece embroidered with gold and silk threads features the Virgin surrounded by St. Vivant and St. Peter;

204

205

Drawn with Indian ink on white silk, this mitre comes from the Sainte-Chapelle in Paris. Featured on the front is the Resurrection, while on the back is the Entombment, both treated in a style reminiscent of Parisian painting between 1350 and 1370 and the famous Narbonne Altarcloth (Musée du Louvre). The kneeling religious figure remains unidentified.

205 **Alms-purse
of Marie de Picquigny**

Recently restored to its original appearance, this linen alms-purse was embroidered with silk and metal thread. The coats of arms show it was made for Marie de Picquigny, who married Jean d'Hangest in 1342, which thus provides a dating for the piece.

206

207

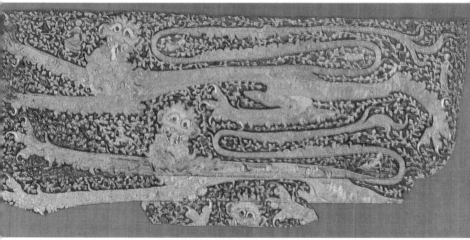

208

207 **Embroidered mitre**

France (Paris?), XIVth century
Silk, silver and gold thread, pearls
H 37 cm; W 30 cm
A. Lenoir Coll.
National Archives Deposit, 1892;
CL 12923

The technique of this exceptional embroidered mitre, inventoried in 1480 at the Sainte-Chapelle, sought to compete with goldsmithery in its relief, pearls, coloured glass, its now non-existent "plique" enamels and even the architectural decor. It is probably an early XIVth-century Parisian work.

English fabrics

English production was so prolific and its success so outstanding that the term "opus anglicanum" rapidly compelled recognition, although the exact technique sometimes remained obscure. It cannot be limited to the spiralling split stitch, despite the extraordinary works of art it produced that could rival with painting. As often happened, the term came to designate a technique, while the place

of manufacture was overlooked. There is no question of confining English production to this technique alone during its most remarkable era (end of XIIIth-XIVth century), even when manifest in superb gifts. The sumptuousness, number, importance of metal thread and quality of these works are detailed in inventories from the period.

208 **Embroidery with leopards**

England, first third of XIVth century
Silk, partially gilded silver thread,
cabochons, pearls
H 51 cm; L 124 cm
Acq. 1922; CL 20367

The leopards of England, young girls and foliated scrolls feature on this piece of velvet embroidered in gold and multicoloured silk thread. From its style and technique, it can be attributed to an English workshop and given a dating of the first third of the XIVth century. Transformed into a chasuble in the XVIIIth century, it may initially have been a horsecloth.

209

Flemish fabrics

What has already been said about the relationship between painting and French textiles also applies to Flemish production, and more specifically to its greatest works. The pieces from the late period catalogued today were designed by painters, who employed highly-skilled craftsmen capable of conveying the spirit of the works. Wool, silk and metal were versatile enough to comply with the demand. In this respect, fabrics entered the realm of tapestry.

209 **Antependium of Mechlin**

> Meuse region, first half of XIVth century
> Linen, silk and metal thread
> H 82.5 cm; L 186.5 cm
> Mechlin Civil Hospital (?)
> Gift of A. de Rothschild, 1889; CL 11995

A recent study has pinpointed this altar frontal's origin to Mechlin (Civil Hospital?), and given an early XIVth-century dating. The embroidery on the linen drill is in poor condition, the silk and metal threads having been lost and replaced. The use of the flat stitch is characteristic of the Meuse region, while the iconography is no less original; from left to right: St. Martin,

St. Mark, St. John the Evangelist asleep on Christ's breast, St. John drinking the poison.

210 **St. Christopher. Two porters**

> Flanders, end of XVth century
> Linen, silk, gold
> H 36.4 cm; L 30.7 cm (CL 1843)
> H 37.3 cm; L 32.7 cm (CL 1844)
> Acq. 1850; CL 1843 and CL 1844

The two small linen panels embroidered in silk and metal thread depicting St. Christo

210

211

212

pher and two unidentified figures are Flemish works from the very end of the XVth century.

211 Chasuble: Jesse Tree

Italy, XVth century (velvet background) and Flanders, second half of XVth century (embroidered orphrey)
Silk, gold thread
H 120.5 cm; L 64 cm
Gift of Guy Ladrière, 1986; CL 23269

The original chasuble was recut during the classical period into the then customary violin-shaped form. Made out of a fine Italian velvet, it was decorated with an orphrey that featured a Jesse Tree whose very refined style and technique denote a probable Flemish origin from the second half of the XVth century.

212 Chasuble: Crucifixion between angels

Italy, XVth century (velvet background) and Flanders, end of XVth century (embroidered orphrey)
Linen, gold, silver and silk thread
Front: H 116.5 cm; L 77 cm
Back: H 121.9 cm; L 79.8 cm
Du Sommerard collection; CL 1219

The two strips of embroidered orphrey, no doubt of Flemish origin from the late XVth century, were mounted on a XVth-century Venetian velvet brocade. Following common practice, the chasuble was later recut during the classical period.

213

German fabrics

Close ties existed between German textiles and their destination, at least during the early period. Pieces intended for religious use are thought to have been executed by the skilled hands of convent members, while outside artists were called upon to supply easily transportable cartoons for the creation of the finest works.

213 Altar frontal of Huysbourg

Germany (Lower Saxony), circa 1150-1160
Linen, silk thread
H 72.5 cm; L 49 cm
Monastery of Huysbourg
Acq. 1860; CL 3048

The three incomplete fragments featuring apostles under arcades were part of a larger composition, now dispersed, which came from the monastery of Huysbourg, near Halberstadt. This embroidery might ini-

tially have been a hanging or an antependium and is thought to have been executed in Lower Saxony around 1150-1160.

Tapestries

Our knowledge of the origin and history of medieval tapestry has been thoroughly updated in the last few years, following a certain number of discoveries that have focused attention on both economic and stylistic factors.

The technique was indeed an ancient one, but, from the mid-XIVth to the XVth century, production was constantly on the increase. Initiated by a policy of the Duke of Burgundy, who was anxious to replace a cloth industry beset by competitors with a new luxury, semi-luxury, or even common industry. Trade and sales were encouraged by bankers, important entrepreneurs and even the markets.

Manufacturing centres were so diverse that it is hard to pinpoint a piece's origin when not confirmed by a document. The major centres were Arras, Lille, Tournai and above all Brussels, which took the lead in the XVIth century in terms of quantity and quality; but there were also home industries under sub-

214

contract to workshops unable to meet demand, which further complicates matters.

A certain homogeneity can however be explained by the fact that weavers were willing to go from one workshop to another, from one town to another, either through personal choice or in answer to a specific demand for labour. The history of medieval tapestry thus involves more than merely locating where a piece was manufactured.

Tapestry fell primarily within an industrial context of mass-production, where rapid turnover was a decisive element in its success. But there were also commissioned works, arranged by verbal or written agreement between the purchaser and the manufacturer or merchant. They can be recognised from their individuality, often marked by coats of arms (Lady with the Unicorn, choir-hanging in the Cathedrals of Auxerre, Bayeux and Beauvais). Style and iconography therefore depended on personal choice.

As a rule, a tapestry was completed in three stages: first the model maker drew a preliminary design on a reduced scale that might then be coloured; next the cartoonist executed the full-sized design, down to the smallest detail; lastly the weaver set to work at the loom. In the course of these different stages, all possibilities could be envisaged: the model may have been drawn up by a great artist known by the purchaser (Lady with the Unicorn); the cartoonist might reuse former models or use the same design several times in one hanging (Manorial Life). The weaver himself might intervene in the choice of colours or in the background detail, frequently an allover pattern (millefleurs); to gain time, a tapestry could be made in different workshops, which led to quite perceptible variations (choir hangings of Beauvais, Lérian and Lauréolle).

The majority of the works that have survived are the most ordinary, mass-produced tapestries where priority was given to low production costs, rapid execution and fashionable subjects. The finest hangings with silk, silver and gilded silver thread have almost all

214   **The Resurrection**

Arras (?), circa 1420
Silk and metal
H 77 cm; L 240 cm
Louvre Deposit; LOA 3132

This altar frontal is distinguished by its early XVth-century dating, by its technique of interwoven silk and metal exclusive of wool and by its style.

disappeared, or are too damaged to be assessed for their quality. The tapestry of David and Bathsheba, *today in the Musée d'Ecouen, is an exceptional example in ten pieces measuring over 70 metres long. It is one of those described as "haute-lisse", or high-warp, in the same way one speaks of haute couture in fashion today. Consequently, it is not a technical definition based on the difference between horizontal and vertical looms, for if the iconography is taken into account, it seems likely that only the former existed during this period.*

215 **The Offering of the Heart**

Arras (?), early XVth century
Wool and silk
H 247 cm; L 209 cm
Exhibited at the Louvre; LOA 3131

This piece, in which a young man literally presents his heart to a seated maiden, is stylistically in tune with what is known as the International Gothic period; this spanned the years around 1400, affected all the great courts of Europe, and is characterised here by the elegant figures and gestures, the taste for muted tones and the unreal aspect of the scene combined with a dream-like setting.

215

216

Choir hangings

216 **The Deliverance of St. Peter**

Tournai (?), 1460
Wool and silk
H 272 cm; L 221 cm
Beauvais Cathedral
Du Sommerard collection; CL 1235

This tapestry that features an angel liberating St. Peter from Herod's prison is the fifth piece of a choir hanging once found in Beauvais Cathedral. It was commissioned in 1460 by its Bishop, Guillaume de Hellande. His coat of arms may be seen on the left, while the chapter's arms are to the right. The word "Paix" no doubt alludes to the truce signed in 1444 by France and England. From the figures' calm attitudes and the fluid lines of the boldly-shadowed drapery, stylistic parallels may be drawn with the work of Jacques Daret, a pupil of Robert Campin active in Tournai.

217 The Tapestry of St. Stephen

Brussels (?), circa 1500
Wool and silk
Illustration: St. Stephen discusses with the
Jewish doctors
H 168 cm; L 359 cm; CL 9930
Auxerre Cathedral
CL 9930-9938; 20200-20201

Formerly hung in Auxerre Cathedral, 45
metres long and in twelve pieces, woven
around 1500 in wool and silk thread, it was
commissioned by Bishop Jean Baillet
whose coat of arms can be recognised. The
subject is the story of St.Stephen, taken
from twenty-three scenes in *The Golden
Legend*, and summarised in the French cap-
tions. The artist created a sequence of
alternating interior and exterior scenes,
vertically separated by architectural or
plant motifs. His concern for detail is
shown in his realistic treatment of nature
and buildings, while a specific rhythm is
built up as one moves from closed spaces to
open horizons. The protagonists are
usually grouped together in the foreground, in compositions inscribed in geometric figures. Despite the brutality of certain scenes, there is a pervasive calmness
explicit in the body movement and the
harmonious flow of gestures. The rich bro-
cades and iridescent colours of the clothing
reveal the painstaking attention paid to
detail. The weaver took great care to accen-
tuate light and shade, carving volumes out
of space. In every respect, the painter who
designed this hanging was greatly influenced by the Brussels artist Colyn de Coter.

217

Textiles

218 (detail)

218 **The Tapestry of St. Quentin**

Brussels (?), end of XVth century
Wool and silk
H 330 cm; L 790 cm
Basilica of St. Quentin
Exhibited at the Louvre; LOA Rev. 825

This choir hanging comes from the Basilica of St. Quentin. True to its genre, it illustrates the life of the saint in a series of anecdotes, each one related by a legend in the Picard dialect. In fact, it depicts one of the miracles performed by the saint whose shrine is featured. Made in the last third of the XVth century, it originally included other pieces.

219 Choir hanging from the Cathedral of Bayeux

Paris (cartoons), pre-1499
Wool and silk
H 130 cm; L 73 cm
Bayeux Cathedral
Bacri Donation, 1972; CL 22866

As explained by the inscription on the first piece, the hanging devoted to the life of the Virgin was a gift made in 1499 by chancellor Léon Conseil. It was initially composed of six pieces; in addition to the fragments displayed here, depicting the Annunciation, the Visitation, the Virgin and St. Joseph, others exist in the United States. The style recalls unidentified Parisian engravings of the same period that appeared in printed books.

219

220 The Lady with the Unicorn

Paris (cartoons), the Netherlands
(weaving), 1484-1500
Wool and silk
Acq. 1882; CL 10831-10834
Illustrations: Taste
H 377 cm; L 466 cm
CL 10831
A Mon Seul Désir (To my Sole Desire)
H 377 cm; L 473 cm
CL 10834

The tapestries of *La Dame à la Licorne (The Lady with the Unicorn)* series were acquired in 1882, after having hung for nearly two hundred years in the Château of Boussac (Creuse). Research has elucidated their origin, iconography and style.
The coat of arms - Gules a Bend Azure charged with three Crescents Argent - has long been identified as those of the Le Viste family of Lyons, whose members pursued brilliant legal careers. They settled in Paris in the XVth century and distinguished themselves in royal office and in Parliament. Barthélémy became counsellor in 1440, to be succeeded in this function by his son Aymé, who died in 1484, leaving two sons; the elder son, Jean, appointed to the highest office of the Court of Appeals in 1471, died without leaving a male heir in 1500, as President of the Court of Aids. Modern scholars esteem that it was Jean Le Viste who commissioned the tapestry, no doubt between 1484, the date at which he took over the full family arms on the death of his father, and 1500, the date of his own death.
The iconography has now been elucidated, since it has been established that the six pieces constituted the entire series and that this was the order in which they were hung at the Château de Boussac. Five of them depict the senses, a theme not uncommon in the Middle Ages:

"Sight": the unicorn gazes at itself in a mirror held by the young woman;

"Hearing": the Lady plays a portable organ while her maidservant pumps the bellows;

Textiles

220 « Taste »

"Taste": the young woman chooses a sweet from a dish, while the parakeet holds one in its claws and a monkey below takes one to its mouth;

"Smell": the Lady makes a garland of carnations, while a monkey presses one he has stolen from the basket to his nose;

"Touch": with her left hand, the young woman delicately holds the horn of the unicorn.

"A Mon Seul Désir"

The sixth piece, which depicts the Lady standing in front of a majestic tent with open flaps, for a long time defied all interpretation. Contrary to what has always been thought, she is in fact not selecting, but depositing the necklace into the casket held by her maidservant, and holding it in a cloth, after having taken it off. She is thus not in the act of choosing a piece of jewellery, but of renouncing her jewels. In the light of this reading, the inscription at the top of the tent, "A mon seul désir" (to my sole desire), becomes self-explanatory and gives the key to the meaning of her gesture. This scene is related to the idea of *liberum arbitrium,* considered by philosophers of Antiquity as being the faculty which leads us to right action, unless it is hindered by the passions, that is by our capitulation to the senses. This interpretation might seem precarious, were it not confirmed by another example, also a tapestry: in the rich collections of the Cardinal de La Marck was a series of tapestries known as *Los Sentidos*; five of them depicted the senses and the sixth bore the inscription *Liberum arbitrium.*

The Cluny tapestries offer a further reading involving the heraldic symbols. The insistent repetition of Jean Le Viste's arms

220 «A Mon Seul Désir»

calls for an explanation: they are represented as many as four times in "Smell" and "Taste", while the lances with banners and pennants are weapons, because they end in sharp points. The tent in the sixth piece was more a feature of the battlefield than of domestic life. This association of arms with a profane and peaceful allegory was how Jean de Viste manifested his pretensions to nobility, which would however remain unsatisfied. In his will, he went so far as to ask to be represented on a stained-glass window in his chapel "as a knight in armour". This man of law who was rewarded with the highest honours, including the supreme honour of being buried in the chapel of the Célestins in Paris, like so many of his contemporaries from the provinces, fervently aspired to the spheres of nobility. He was among those whose hopes were not to be fulfilled.

The Lady with the Unicorn owes its fame to its harmonious colour scheme. A limited number of shading off tones were used to render the many different elements of the composition. This restrained palette helps to create the feeling of poetic enchantment. The dark-blue, rounded "isle" which serves as a ground for each scene is strewn with flowering plants, while the background that ranges in colour from red to pink, is scattered with blossoming branches torn from their bough. This kind of decor is recorded as having been frequent in medieval tapestries, but few of the pieces themselves have survived. This marvellous decor highlights the elegance of the young woman, who appears in different attitudes and costumes, the splendour of which further enhances the great beauty of this work.

opposite : 220 «Hearing» (detail)

221

221 La Vie Seigneuriale (Manorial Life)

Southern Netherlands, circa 1500-1525
Wool and silk
H 258 cm; L 174 cm
Acq. 1852; CL 2183

The six pieces of *La Vie Seigneuriale* (incomplete) constitute what was known at the time as a "tapestry room", the different scenes of which are easily recognised: "The Promenade", "Scenes of Courting", "The Bath", "Embroidery", "Reading" and "Departure for the Hunt". Characteristic of the style then in vogue, the millefleur background sets off the floating silhouettes of the figures that are reused at will to save labour: hence, the young woman carrying a tray in "The Bath" also appears in "The Promenade" and other tapestries. Furthermore, the cartoonist happily borrowed from the leading artists of the period: the fine halberdier in "Departure for the Hunt" was based on a print by Dürer.

222 The Grape Harvest

Southern Netherlands, early XVIth
century
Wool and silk
H 246 cm; L 495 cm
Dollfuss Legacy, 1930; CL 21541

The Grape Harvest is in fact made up of
two fragments skilfully joined in the centre,
when the coats of arms in the corners at the
top were repaired. This exhibit was part of
a larger tapestry, whose surviving "Picking
the Grapes" scene was a frequently adapted theme. Both fragments have retained
their colours, together with the singular
play of light on the drapery. The style itself
(circa 1500) is reminiscent of that found in
Parisian works, especially printed books.

222 (detail)

223

223 **Arithmetic**

Tournai (?), circa 1520
Wool and silk
H 350 cm; L 294 cm
Acq. 1858; CL 2823

This tapestry was part of a hanging that
illustrated the liberal arts; it remains uncer-
tain whether the various pieces, dispersed
throughout France and abroad, come from
the same work, even if the models and
cartoons were made by the same artists,
doubtless close to the artistic circle responsible for *The Prodigal Son.*

224 Departure of the Prodigal Son

Tournai (?), circa 1520
Wool and silk
H 362 cm; L 668 cm
Acq. 1844; CL 1495

This piece depicts the beginning of the parable of the Prodigal Son: the son's departure, his family, including his brother, his close ones; the journey; his life of debauchery; each scene is separated by a surbased arcade on decorative supports. The artist used perspective to add a sense of space to each episode. He thus lowered the foreground, by giving it a millefleur treatment, before developing a vast mountainous landscape that gives way to the sky. Like *Arithmetic*, this 1520s piece is enhanced by its palette, its muted tones and its effects of light and shade.

224

225 The Embarkation

Brussels, circa 1500-1525
Wool and silk
H 273 cm; L 317 cm
Inv. in 1905; CL 14335

This tapestry fragment featuring a battle and an embarkation depicts characters who lived centuries apart: Dido and Aeneas, Iulus and Calchas, Cambyses or Totila. Added to the iconographical complexity is the work's fragmented state. Nevertheless, the origin of the caravel is clear: an engraving by Master WA, a Flemish artist active in Bruges around 1465-1485, must have inspired the model maker in the first quarter of the XVIth century.

225

226 Lérian and Lauréolle

Southern Netherlands, circa 1500-1525
Wool and silk
Acq. 1956; CL 22742
Illustration: Royal Inflexibility
H 415 cm; L 483 cm
Acq. 1986; CL 23249

The acquisition of a piece from the tapestry of The Story of Lérian and Lauréolle enables us to compare two works woven from models by the same cartoonist, but produced separately in the first quarter of the XVIth century - Royal Inflexibility and The Royal Pardon - inspired from the *Carcel del Amor* by Diego di San Pedro, a Spanish poet of the second half of the XVth century, who was extremely popular in the first half of the XVIth century. Stylistically, it can be paralleled with Flemish painting.

226 (details)

227 Scenes of Triumph and the Death of Honour

Southern Netherlands, circa 1500-1525
Wool and silk
CL 14336, 14337, 17009, 22594
Illustration: The Death of Honour
H 195 cm; L 208 cm
Du Sommerard collection, inv. in 1905;
CL 14336

Four pieces - three fragmented, only one complete - depict one of the themes evoked by XVth and XVIth-century poets: the immortality of the soul gained by a virtuous life. Inscriptions and legends facilitate interpretation of the scenes whose iconography is sometimes obscure. These four tapestries were, in fact, works produced between 1500 and 1525 from the same models. A more exact dating cannot be given from the stereotype style.

227

228

228 Daniel and Nebuchadnezzar

Tournai (?), early XVIth century
Wool and silk
H 347 cm; L 619 cm
Acq. 1847; CL 1630

This piece illustrates scenes from the story
of Daniel and Nebuchadnezzar. On the
right is the episode of the composite statue;
on the left are Nebuchadnezzar's soldiers,
under orders to destroy the wise men of
Babylon, and Daniel who intervenes.

Index

Index of names and iconographical themes, with reference numbers of exhibits listed in this guide.

Iconographical Themes

(Frequently adopted iconographical themes, such as the Crucifixion or the Virgin and Child, have been omitted.)

Bibliography

**Catalogues from the
National Museum of the Middle Ages -
The Roman Baths of Cluny**

Jean-Pierre Caillet
*L'Antiquité classique, le haut Moyen Age
et Byzance au musée de Cluny*, Paris,
Réunion des musées nationaux, 1985.

Alain Erlande-Brandenburg
*Les Sculptures de Notre-Dame de Paris
au musée de Cluny*, Paris, Réunion
des musées nationaux, 1982.

Fabienne Joubert
*La Tapisserie médiévale au musée
de Cluny*, Paris, Réunion des musées
nationaux, 1987.

Victor Klagsbald
*Catalogue raisonné de la collection juive
du musée de Cluny*, Paris, Réunion
des musées nationaux, 1981.

Alexandra Lorquin
*Les Tissus coptes du musée national du
Moyen Age - Thermes de Cluny. Etoffes
de lin et de laine*, Paris, Réunion
des musées nationaux, 1992.

Elisabeth Taburet-Delahaye
*L'Orfèvrerie gothique (XIIIᵉ-début XVᵉ s.)
au musée de Cluny*, Paris, Réunion
des musées nationaux, 1989.

Photographic credits:

Réunion des Musées Nationaux, Paris
except for
Jacques Lebar, Paris, 62, 66, 188, 192

Graphic design and layout: Bruno Pfäffli
Coordinating editor: Josette Grandazzi
Translator: Pamela Hargreaves
Photocomposition: A.P.S., Tours
Photoengraving: Bussière A.G., Paris
Printed by Mame, Tours

ISBN 2-7118-2777-1
GG 20 2777